INSIDE OUT

INSIDE OUT

THE WONDERS OF MODERN TECHNOLOGY

CAROL J. AMATO

ILLUSTRATIONS BY BILL LOMBARDO

SMITHMARK

A FRIEDMAN GROUP BOOK

This edition published in 1992
by SMITHMARK Publishers Inc.
16 East 32nd Street
New York, New York 10016

ISBN 0-8317-4657-2

INSIDE OUT
The Wonders of Modern Technology
was prepared and produced by
Michael Friedman Publishing Group, Inc.
15 West 26th Street
New York, NY 10010

Editor: Sharyn Rosart
Art Direction: Devorah Levinrad
Photography Researcher: Grace How

Typeset by Typecrafters, Inc.
Color separations by Rainbow Graphic Arts Co.
Printed and bound in Singapore by Tien Wah Press

SMITHMARK Books are available for bulk purchase for
sales promotions and premium use. For details write or
telephone the Manager of Special Sales,
SMITHMARK Publishers Inc., 16 East 32nd Street,
New York, New York 10016, (212) 532-6600.

This book is dedicated to all the scientists, researchers, and inventors whose wonderful discoveries have made the world a healthier and more exciting place to live.

CONTENTS

PART ONE
AIR AND SPACE TECHNOLOGY   12

PART TWO
COMMUNICATIONS TECHNOLOGY 50

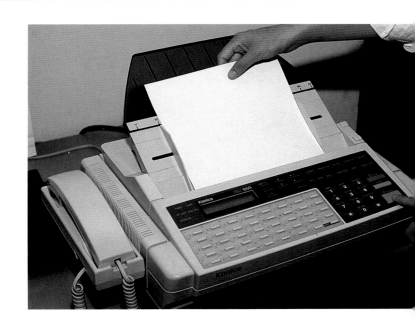

PART THREE
MEDICAL TECHNOLOGY 84

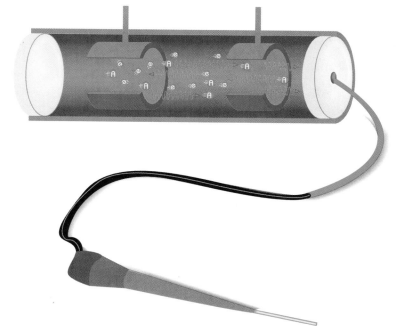

PART FOUR
HOUSEHOLD TECHNOLOGY 98

INTRODUCTION

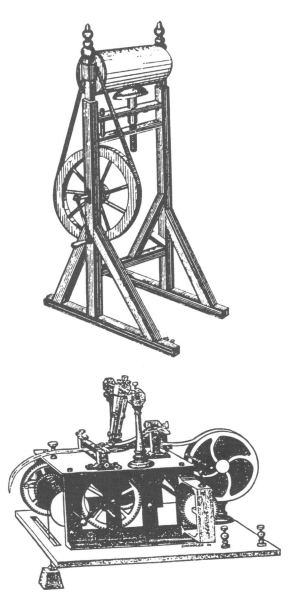

Ben Franklin used this electrostatic machine (top) in his experiments with electricity and conductivity in the late 1840s. By the mid-1850s, numerous telegraph systems had been developed, including an igniting model (bottom), but the basic patent belonged to Samuel Morse.

Humans have been on the earth for approximately 3 million years, yet technology as we use the word today (electronic and mechanical advancement) has developed more in the last 250 years than it did in all the previous years.

Just 250 years ago, there were no mechanized factories, no telegraphs, no trains, no steamships and, of course, no airplanes, cars, telephones, electricity, or flush toilets. The Industrial Revolution brought about a "quantum leap" in technological development that made all of these other discoveries possible.

Technological development can be divided into four main eras. The first is from the dawn of humanity up to 1760, when virtually no technological progress of note occurred other than the invention of the printing press. The second period spans the years from 1760 to 1900, the era of the Industrial Revolution, during which most technological development occurred in factory settings. The third period is from 1900 to 1950, the era that ushered in the airplane, automobile, telephone, record player, and a host of other "newfangled" inventions. The fourth period began in 1950 and continues to the present, an age that has seen yet another revolution in technological development: the advent of the space program, computers, and the communications revolution.

The Industrial Revolution first began in Great Britain in 1760. It was a result of several factors: the expansion of commerce that had begun in the Middle Ages; the opening of the Middle East to European trade after the Crusades; and the more open-minded attitude that developed during the Renaissance, which prompted scientists to experiment and make new discoveries.

The United States experienced its Industrial Revolution much later, in the latter half of the 1800s, as did Germany, after 1870. The result of all three was the same, however; the national economies, previously based on agriculture, became industrial.

Though mechanized factories became commonplace during the Industrial Revolution, people still lived in houses without electricity, running water, or heat except for that provided by wood stoves or fireplaces, and they used kerosene lamps and candles for light. Medical science hadn't advanced sufficiently to prevent women from routinely dying in childbirth. Steam trains, steamships, horses, carriages, and stagecoaches were the major forms of transportation, and the mail was delivered by Pony Express, boat, and stagecoach.

By the late 1800s, however, scientists were encouraged to make new discoveries, and mechanization was becoming commonplace; as a result, the

On view in Machinery Hall at the 1876 American Centennial exhibition was the Hoe Company's "Web Printing Machine," which was capable of printing 25,000 sheets an hour. Isaac M. Singer was one of three mid-century inventors to build a sewing machine (bottom). His design received a patent in 1851.

rate of technological change began to increase. Thomas Edison was hard at work, not only improving the quality of telegraph transmission, but inventing such contraptions as the phonograph, the electric light bulb, and the kinetoscope, the first machine to produce motion pictures by showing a rapid succession of individual images. In the meantime, Alexander Graham Bell was busy inventing the telephone. The world was separated into time zones, and people no longer had to set their clocks by the sun.

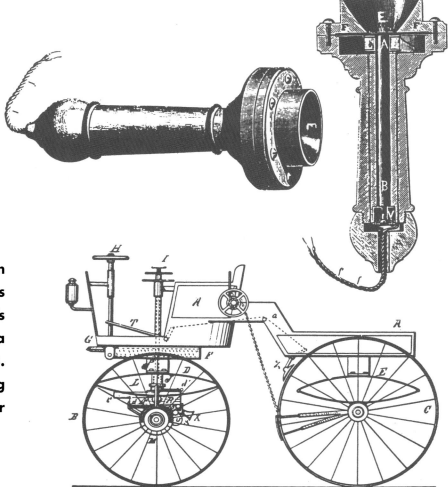

Sir Humphry Davy designed an electric light (below) as early as 1910. Alexander Graham Bell's telephone (right, top) was granted a patent in 1876. By 1879, George B. Selden had invented a working internal combustion engine to power a "horseless carriage."

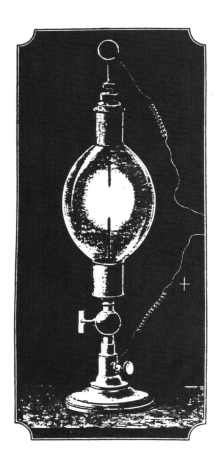

The rate of change increased even more after 1900. Not only did electric lights and telephones and indoor plumbing begin to appear in homes in the cities, but the automobile was built. Once Henry Ford began using mass-production techniques, the price lowered until cars became affordable for many people. The Wright brothers made their historic flight, heralding the era of the airplane, and Hollywood began churning out silent movies.

Even so, some inventions were slow to catch on. For instance, although Edison combined his phonograph and kinetoscope to make the first talking motion picture in 1913, Hollywood didn't produce its first "talkie" until *The Jazz Singer* in 1927! Similarly, although few people really saw the need for airplanes at the time of the Wright brothers' flight, just a few years later, during World War I, they proved indispensable. Only after the war was any thought given to their use as a means of commercial transportation, although the prevailing attitude held that airplanes would never be any good for long-distance travel. After all, the amount of fuel necessary would be so heavy the plane could never get off the ground. How could any of these people have foreseen the coming of jet fuel?

Once started, technological advancement continued rapidly. John Logie Baird, an Englishman, developed the first device that transmitted television signals. In 1932, Walt Disney made the first color movie. Penicillin was invented in 1939. The first jet flight took place in 1941.

IBM launched a historic invention in 1944—the Automatic Sequence Controlled Calculator (ASCC), which was the prototype of the modern computer. This monster didn't fit on any desktop, however. The ASCC was 50 feet (15 m) long, weighed 5 tons (4.5 metric t), had nearly 1 million components and 500 miles (800 km) of wire!

Decades became known for the inventions and/or discoveries they spawned: The 1950s saw the development of the Salk polio vaccine, the transistor, the television in the home, and the dawn of the Space Race. The 1960s saw the widespread use of computers in industry; the building of Concorde, the first supersonic transport; and the landing of men on the moon. The 1970s saw the coming of magnetic resonance imaging in medicine, computers that fit on a desktop, and environmental control systems; and the 1980s saw the communications revolution, with the real explosion of personal computers, and the development of fax machines, cellular phones, VCRs, and CD players, in addition to the microwave oven, digital watches, and computerized cars.

Many of our modern inventions can be attributed directly to the materials developed for the space program. Among these spin-offs are the transistor, the computer, artificial joints, pacemakers, Teflon,™ certain kinds of rubber for tires, certain fireproof materials, and communications satellites.

Over the past twenty-five years, technological development has proceeded at an unprecedented rate. Rather than appearing every few years, as they did in the first part of the century, technological innovations seem to appear every few months. Almost as soon as an item is introduced it is replaced by a newer, better model. Once we become used to a new invention, we not only wonder how we ever lived without it, we become totally dependent on it. Could you go back to a world without modern medicine, indoor plumbing, heat, cars, supermarkets, or telephones?

The goal of *Inside Out* is to treat and prevent "Future Shock" by explaining, in very simple terms, how several of these inventions work. Many of the concepts on which these technologies are based are actually very simple. The workings of many common devices are clearly revealed in *Inside Out*, using diagrams and explanations that will demystify the technological wonders of the modern age.

Stages in the evolution of the airplane, from the use of midwing ailerons (1909) to all-metal cantilevered wings (1918) to engines set into the wings (1931) to the delta-wing fighter plane (1953).

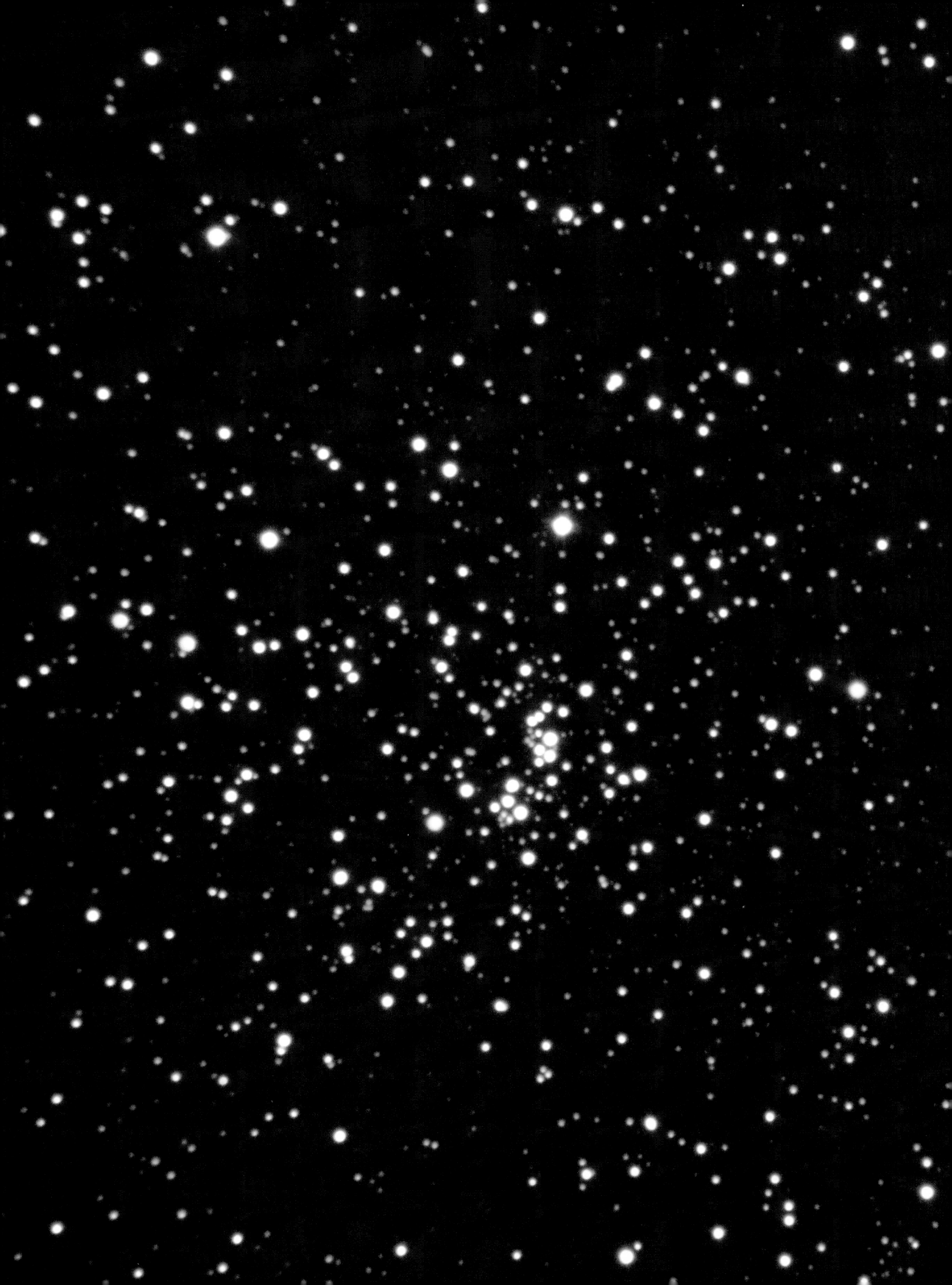

PART ONE

AIR AND SPACE TECHNOLOGY

AIRPLANE

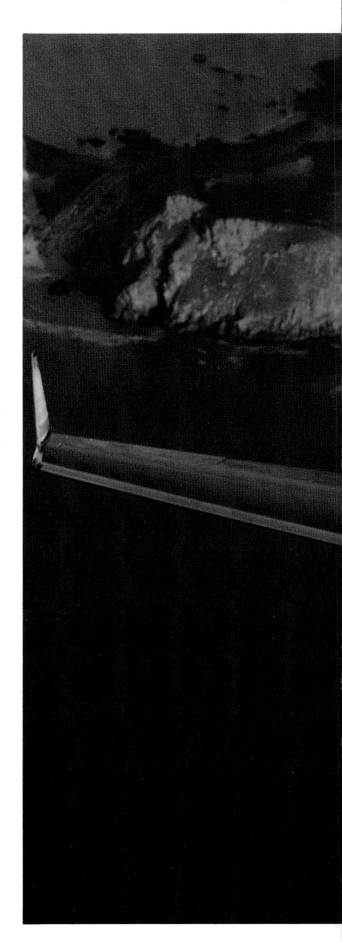

From the moment humans first spotted birds flying and envied their freedom of movement above the planet's surface, the concept of flight has intrigued us.

Just as our forebears once wondered about birds, so have many of us asked, exactly how do airplanes fly? What keeps them from falling back to Earth, given their heavy weight and massive size?

While most people would credit Orville and Wilbur Wright (1871-1948 and 1867-1912 respectively) with discovering the secret of flight, what the brothers actually did was to apply the concepts of people who had considered the questions of flight many years earlier. In the 1500s, artist Leonardo da Vinci (1452-1519) designed some flying machines on paper, although he never attempted to build or test them. Modern experiments have shown, however, that da Vinci's machines would indeed have flown. Swiss scientist Daniel Bernoulli (1700-1782) discovered the principle of the modern wingshape, or "airfoil," back in 1738. Englishman Sir George Cayley (1773-1857) developed the basic form of winged aircraft during the 1800s and flew the first glider in 1849.

Perhaps you have seen film footage of some of the early flying machines. Certainly not worthy of the name airplane, most of these contraptions tried imitating the flapping of a bird's wings, and all failed miserably in their attempts to get off the ground.

The Wright brothers made two significant contributions to flight, the first being that they stopped trying to imitate wing flapping, and instead started to imitate the way eagles soar.

AIRFOIL

What holds the airplane up? Both the eagle and the airplane are kept in the air by air pressure on their wings. The wing section of an airplane, known as the airfoil, is designed to be flat on the bottom and curved on the top. As the air divides to pass over the wing, the teardrop shape increases the amount of air that can pass under the wing and decreases the amount of air that can pass over it. This means that the air has to travel a longer distance over the curved surface than it does over the flat underside. To travel the extra distance over the curved wing, the air speeds up, and as it does so, it loses pressure and weight, thereby becoming lighter.

To take off, the plane's engines move the plane forward, and as the plane moves down the runway, the wing rises into the lighter air, pushed by the heavier air flowing under it, and the body of the plane, of course, goes with it. The air pressure pushing up under the wings is called lift.

Above: Airplanes turn using a combination of aileron and rudder movements. For example, with the rudder left and the left wing down, the plane moves to the left.

AIRPLANE	
1	spoilers
2	wing
3	rudder
4	elevator
5	engine
6	leading edge slats
7	aileron
8	trailing edge flap

Right: In large airliners, movement is controlled by various types of movable flaps. *Spoilers* move up and down to control lift or reduce speed. *Slats* extend forward and down from the leading edge of the wing during takeoff and landing, giving the plane more lift at slow speeds. *Ailerons* are used in turning the plane, to make one wing tilt up while the other tilts down. This is known as banking the wings. Trailing edge *flaps* extend backward and down from the wing. On takeoff, they add lift and on landing they reduce the aircraft's speed. *Elevators* move up and down to make the plane move up and down. The *rudder* is used with the ailerons to help steer the plane.

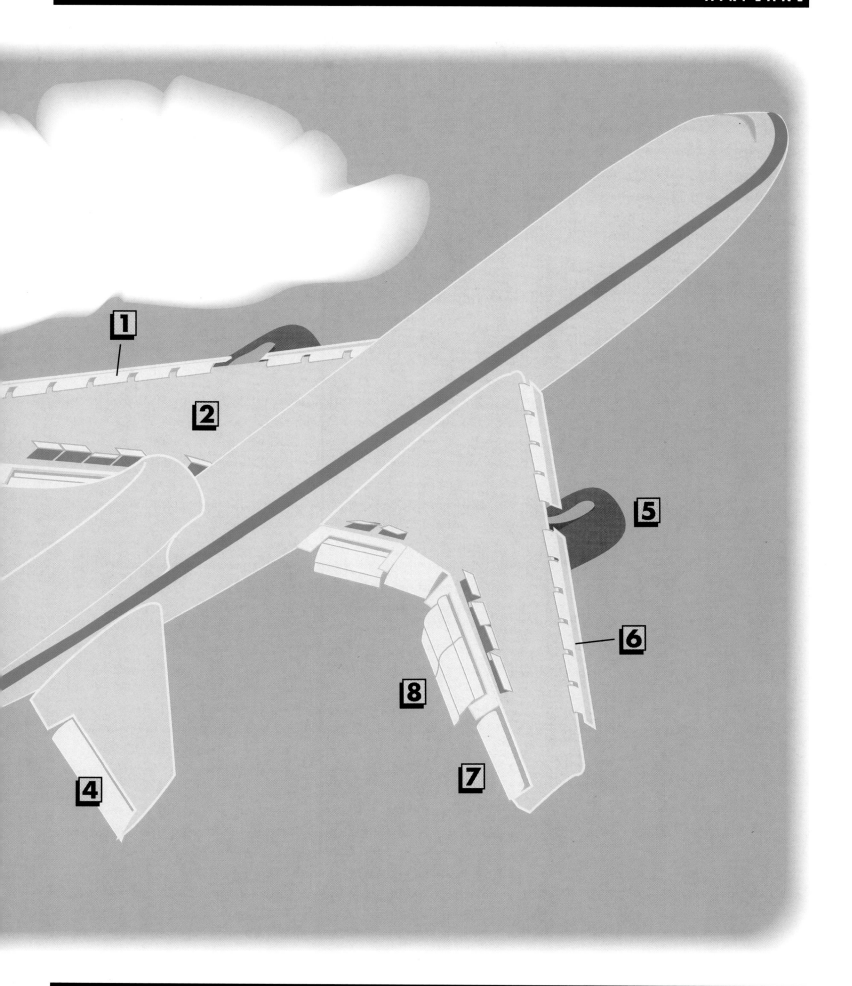

Pitch is the movement of an airplane up and down and is controlled by the elevators. *Yaw* is the left and right movement of the nose, controlled by the rudder. *Roll* is the tilting, or banking, movement of the plane and is controlled by the ailerons.

PITCH, YAW, AND ROLL

1   pitch: nose up and down
2   yaw: nose left and right
3   roll: tilt or flat

The advantage of this type of flight is that the engine need only be powerful enough to overcome the forces of the air sliding past the plane. That means not much power is needed to lift a great deal of weight. In fact, each square foot (9 sq. cm) of a light plane wing can lift 20 to 40 or more pounds (9-18 kg) of airplane into the air.

Forward motion is not enough, however. If it were, race cars would fly; in fact, they are carefully designed so that they do not.

CONTROLS

Because gravity always keeps our feet firmly planted on the ground, human steering and balance systems have evolved in a two-dimensional fashion: sideways and forward/backward. In the air, however, movement is different. The plane moves on three axes, known as pitch, roll, and yaw. Pitch is the movement of the plane's nose up and down; yaw is the movement of the plane's nose left and right; and roll is the movement of one wing up and the other down.

A combination of the pilot's controls, certain parts of the wing, and the rudder are used to direct the pitch, roll, and yaw, and keep the plane properly on course. On the back, or trailing edge, of the wing, are flaps called ailerons. Invented in 1908 by Henry Farman, a British engineer, ailerons are small movable sections of the wing. When the pilot tilts the ailerons up, the wing is forced down. When the pilot tilts the ailerons down, the wing is forced up. In this way, the ailerons control the plane's roll.

On the tail section are similar parts, called the elevators and the rudder, which direct the movement of the plane's nose. The elevators and horizontal stabilizers control the pitch (up and down), while the rudder and the vertical stabilizer control the yaw (left and right).

The pilot's controls consist of a stick, similar to a joystick on a video game, and two pedals that control the rudder on the tail section. In some planes, just like the video game joystick, the pilot's stick can move 360 degrees. In most modern airplanes, however, the stick moves only forward and backward and has a type of steering wheel on its top.

If the pilot pushes the stick forward, the elevators on the tail section lower. The tail then lifts, forcing the plane into a dive. If the pilot pulls back on the stick, the tail section lowers and the nose lifts, and the airplane begins to climb.

Unlike a rudder on a ship, the airplane rudder is not the primary turning control, except when the plane is on the ground. When the plane is in the air, and the pilot pushes the stick or turns the wheel to the left, the left aileron raises and the right aileron lowers. This makes the left wing tilt down and the right one up, and the airplane "banks," or turns, to the left. The pilot applies the rudder (using pedals) on the same side as the ailerons to exert pressure against the air and control the amount of turn. This dis-

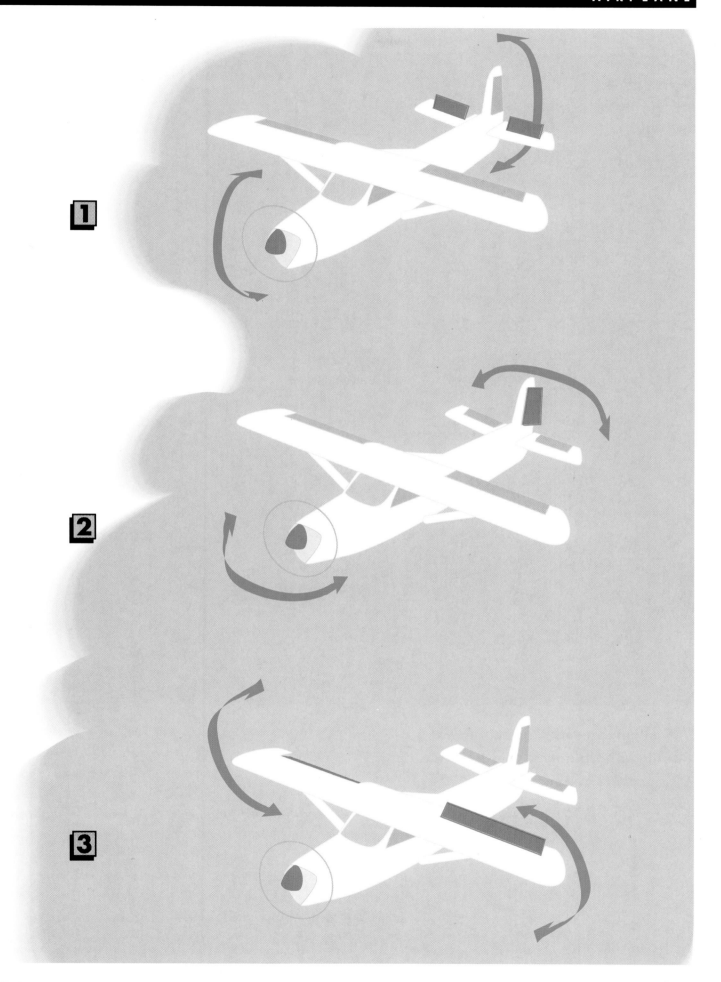

The modern cockpit is an array of digital instruments that monitor the condition and movements of the aircraft.

covery, that a plane turns by banking its wings, was the Wright brothers' other major contribution, considered their greatest to powered flight.

You can try a little experiment yourself to see how air pressure affects an airplane wing. While you are riding along in your car, stick your arm out the window with your palm facing the ground. The air pressure will lift your arm. Next, hold your hand at a right angle to the ground. The air pressure will force your arm backward.

The flaps are the airplane's brakes. These movable surfaces are located on the trailing edge of each wing. In cruising flight, they are retracted. When they are extended, they increase the surface area of the wings, thereby increasing lift. When lift is increased, the airplane can be flown at lower

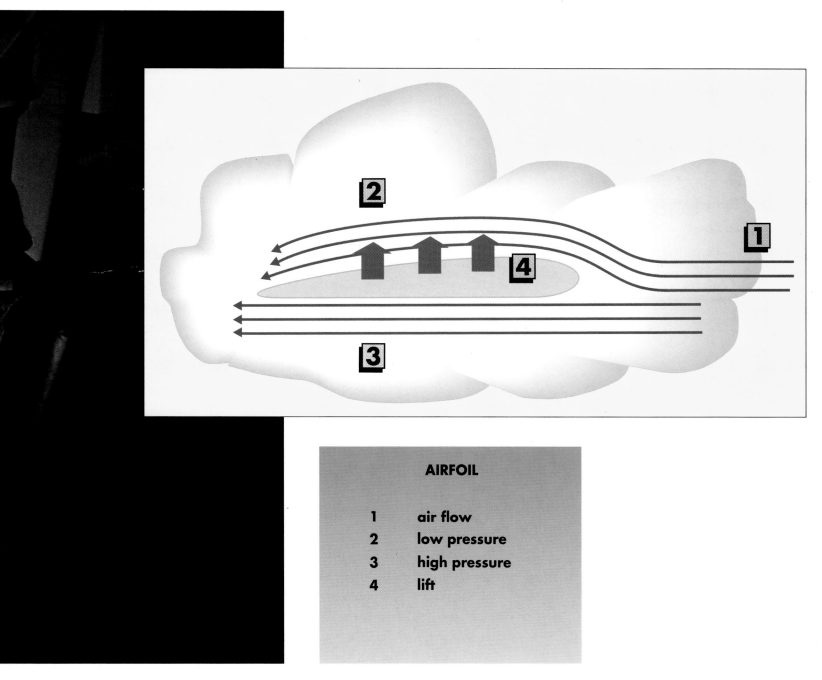

AIRFOIL

1   air flow
2   low pressure
3   high pressure
4   lift

speeds. This increases safety and reduces the length of runway required. Most modern planes have electrically controlled flaps, while those in older planes are hand operated.

What happens when the pilot is in a storm or a cloud bank and can't see the ground? The plane has many other instruments. One of these is the bank-and-turn indicator. This instrument tells the pilot in what direction the plane is turning and at what rate. The directional gyroscope measures the heading of the plane and matches it against a magnetic compass. The gyroscope artificial horizon tells the pilot if the wings are level.

The pilot keeps both feet on the rudder pedals and operates the power controls—mixture, throttle, and propeller pitch—by hand. The mixture con-

Previous page: An airplane wing has the shape of an airfoil. As the wing moves through the air, the airflow divides to pass over and under the wing. The air passing above the wing has to travel farther and faster than that below the wing, causing the air above the wing to thin out. The creates an area of low pressure above the wing, while the denser air below the wing forms an area of high pressure. The differences in air pressure push the wing up—this upward force is called lift.

trol allows adjustments of the fuel-air ratio at different altitudes. The throttle controls the amount of fuel going to the engine (like the accelerator in a car). Since air is thinner at altitudes than it is at sea level (just as it is at higher altitudes on the ground than it is at sea level), less gasoline is needed to maintain the best mixture for combustion.

Airplane engines do not run on car gasoline, however, because the power and cooling needs of a plane are different from those of a car. Most planes have air-cooling fans; oil coolers, since oil absorbs a lot of heat (planes hold more oil in their crankcases than car engines); and cooling by evaporating of the gasoline.

Most American planes have two sets of primary controls. Not only can the plane then be used for flight lessons, but it allows the copilot to take over in the event the pilot cannot fly the plane.

The plane returns to Earth by holding a constant airspeed and remaining at an angle to the ground. The pilot lowers the flaps and landing gear and, using precise gauges, levels the plane out above the runway. The wheels are locked into place, and the plane slows down as the wind hits the landing gear struts and wheels. Finally, when the airplane just won't stay aloft anymore, it touches down onto the runway, and the pilot brings it to a stop.

SUPERSONIC JET

A very exciting milestone in aviation history is the supersonic (faster than sound) jet. Concorde, the supersonic jet developed jointly by France and Britain in the 1960s, is the only commercial form of supersonic travel available. Designed to carry 100 passengers, with two seats on either side of the center aisle, Concorde is a long (204 feet, or 61 m), streamlined airplane with an 84-foot (25-m) delta (V-shaped) wing design. Unlike wings on conventional airplanes, the delta wing design uses no flaps or wing slats.

While military planes have been flying supersonically for almost forty years, commercial supersonic travel became available much later. The United States had planned for supersonic transport (SST) of its own, but Congress refused to approve the funding.

THE CONCORDE

France and Britain, however, independently had plans for a supersonic plane, and rather than duplicate their efforts, formed a partnership in 1962 between British Aircraft Corporation (now British Aerospace) and Aérospatiale, a French aerospace company. Each country manufactured ten Concordes: one prototype, one preproduction version, and eight production aircraft. The French prototype, Concorde 001, first flew on March 2, 1969, at Toulouse, France, while the first flight of the British prototype, Concorde 002, was on April 9 of the same year. The French plane now resides in an air museum at Le Bourget, and the British plane is on display in Yeovilton,

England. Five thousand hours of testing went into Concorde, making it the most tested aircraft in history.

British Airways' first commercial flight was from London to Bahrain, in the Persian Gulf, on January 21, 1976. In November 1986, Concorde made its first round-the-world flight via New York, San Francisco, Honolulu, Guam, Hong Kong, Bali, and Cairo. This 25,000-mile (40,000-km) trip was accomplished in 28 hours and 30 minutes. The regular routes for this aircraft are London to New York, and London to Washington, D.C., but on special trips, Concorde has landed at more than 148 destinations, including cities in Canada, Australia, New Zealand, Singapore, Brazil, the Persian Gulf, and South Africa; and in the United States, Seattle, Pittsburgh, Fort Lauderdale, Houston, Detroit, Asheville, Little Rock, Memphis, Nashville, Wilmington, Cincinnati, and Providence. In the first ten years of its service, Concorde flew more airline passengers at Mach 2 than the number of military pilots who had flown supersonic aircraft worldwide.

SUPERSONIC FLIGHT

Concorde's takeoff is very different from that of a conventional aircraft. Conventional airplanes take off with a subsonic (slower than the speed of sound) speed of 165 knots, or 143 miles per hour (228 km/h). As a supersonic transport, Concorde leaves the runway at 200 to 215 knots, or 173 to 186 miles per hour (277 to 298 km/h)! Despite this difference, however, the length of the runway is the same for both types of planes. Because of the Concorde's delta-shaped wings, lift is very low—meaning that takeoff speed must be high.

Concorde, the world's only commercial supersonic transport, is readily distinguishable by its delta or triangle-shaped wings and its distinctive nose design.

Concorde's cockpit holds a dazzling array of instuments and monitors.

Concorde has four specially developed engines. These modified Rolls-Royce Snecma Olympus 593s give more than 38,000 pounds (17,000 kg) of thrust each, and have afterburners, which add fuel to the final stage of the engine cycle to produce the extra power required for takeoff and transition to supersonic flight.

Concorde's landing speeds are also faster than those of conventional aircraft, and there is a distinctive droop of the nose when the airplane lands, as the nose actually moves out of the pilot's way to improve visibility.

Like Superman, Concorde is literally faster than a speeding bullet, cruising along at Mach 2, which is 1,350 miles per hour (2,160 km/h), or twice the speed of sound. Due to the heating of the airframe in supersonic flight, its normal length stretches almost 10 inches (25 cm).

Traveling at Mach 2 means the plane crosses the Atlantic, a trip of 3,660 miles (5,856 km) in an average of only three hours, twenty-five minutes. Subsonic planes fly this same distance in six-and-a-half to seven-and-a-half hours. Traveling westward, the five-hour time difference between Britain and the United States' East Coast means Concorde arrives before it leaves—at least in local time. As a bonus, the dramatically reduced flight times eliminate jet lag.

While subsonic jets cruise at an altitude of 39,000 feet (11,700 m), Concorde's altitude is some 50,000 to 60,000 feet (15,000-18,000 m). The cabin is pressurized at 4,900 to 5,900 feet (14,700-17,700 m), which is a more comfortable level than the 7,250 feet (2,175 m) on long-distance subsonic flights. In addition, Concorde's cruising altitude is well above that of not only slower jets, thereby reducing air traffic control problems, but above the weather, too.

The research and development that went into Concorde produced more than just an airplane. It resulted in a number of other breakthroughs, among them the use of laser-beam technology in medicine, which will be discussed later in this book.

The delta-wing shape generates less lift than the traditional airfoil wings, requiring Concorde to achieve a higher takeoff speed than non-supersonic jets.

With a proportional rate marine autopilot system, the autopilot sensors can detect a heading error before the craft moves significantly off-course. The autopilot keeps the boat on course by constantly monitoring and, if necessary, adjusting the rudder position.

MARINE AUTOPILOT

1	autopilot controller
2	control buttons
3	heading display
4	lines to motor to correct course
5	boat heading error
6	correct heading
7	corrected heading

AUTOPILOT

An autopilot system is an automatic system for controlling the heading, or "attitude," of a moving vehicle or object—that is, keeping the vehicle on course. Autopilot systems are most often used in airplanes and boats.

The typical autopilot uses instruments called "accelerometers" that measure acceleration, or the rate of change of speed. These accelerometers are mounted on a level platform and stabilized by gyroscopes, which are rotating bodies that help to keep the accelerometer constantly level. Accelerometers operate using the principle of inertia; that is, they sense any force that alters the vehicle's attitude or direction. When the deviation from course occurs, coils located under the accelerometer move, causing an electric signal in the instrument's outer coils. These accelerometer signals then travel to the controls of the aircraft or ship, which correct its course.

MARINE AUTOPILOTS

Autopilot systems actually do more than just monitor movement. In boats, the autopilot not only keeps the vessel on a preselected course, but it serves as a direct or remote-controlled power steering system. This allows the boat's captain to focus attention elsewhere, if necessary. And since the autopilot maintains a more accurate course, savings in fuel and an increase in range are other benefits.

There are three types of marine autopilots, most often used on boats from 18 to 125 feet (5.4-37.5 m) long: hunting, non-hunting proportional deadband, and non-hunting proportional rate.

The hunting autopilot was originally developed in the 1930s, and is considered the original marine autopilot design. The helm is continually moved port and starboard (left and right) through a small angle. A compass detects the amount of the boat's heading error (change or direction off course), and the helm then steers the boat in a direction that corrects the error. As this occurs, the boat moves past the correct direction to the other side of the angle. The helm then corrects in the other direction, "hunting" for the desired direction, controlling the boat in a zigzag movement.

The Hunting autopilot is working all the time, consuming a great deal of power and causing excessive wear and tear on the steering and pilot systems.

The non-hunting proportional deadband autopilot was developed in the 1940s, and it improved on the hunting autopilot by adding a "deadband" into the system. Within this deadband, or zone, the helm is inactive. When the boat gets off course and begins heading out of this zone, however, the

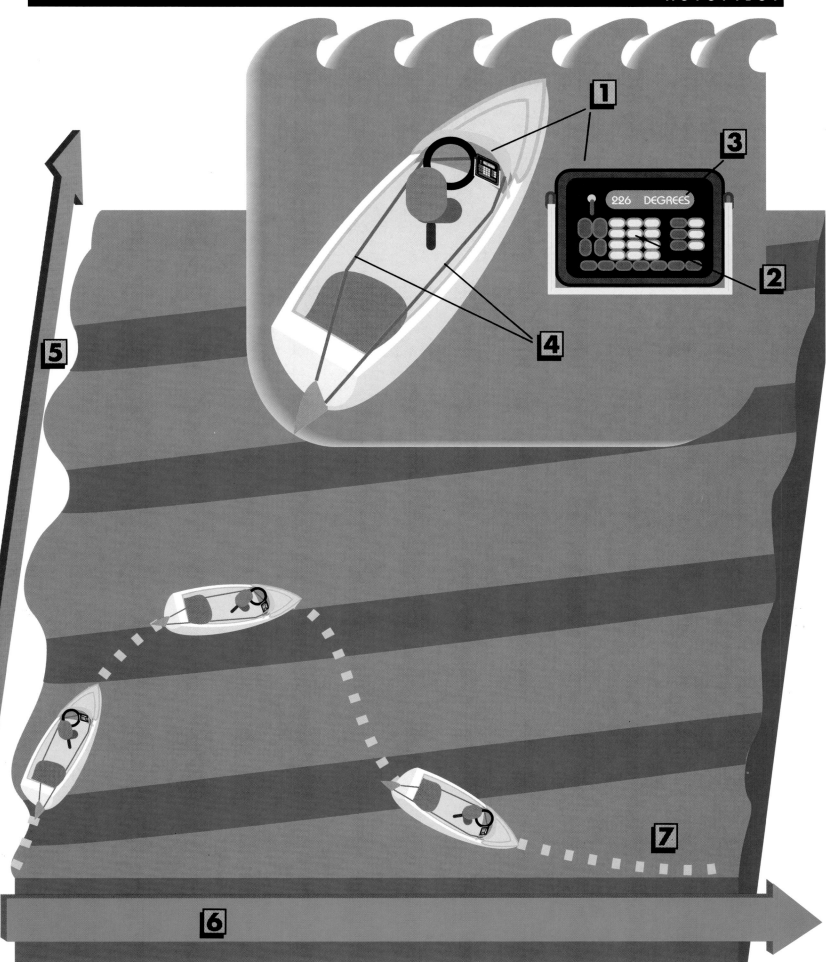

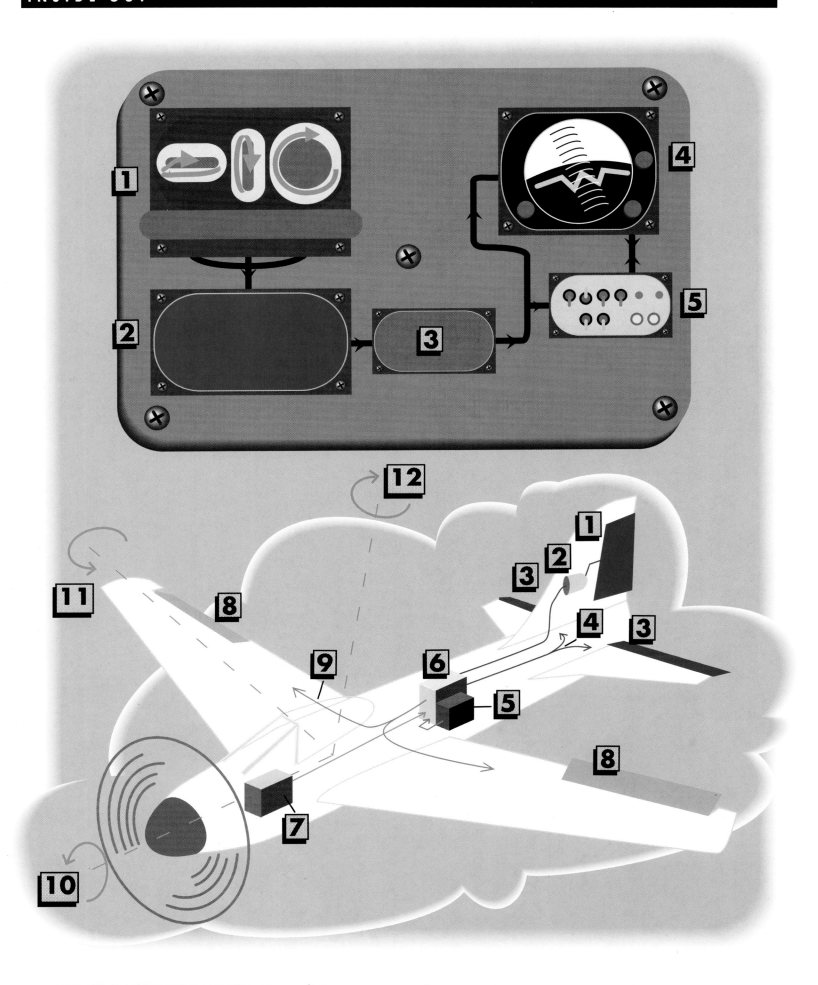

helm is moved in the appropriate direction by an amount that will bring it back on course. If the boat stays on course within the deadband, the autopilot is not activated. The majority of current marine autopilot designs use this proportional deadband principle. This type of autopilot was also used by aircraft in the early days, but was eventually discarded in favor of the non-hunting proportional rate autopilot. The proportional rate system was introduced to marine autopilots in 1975. No deadband is used; instead, the autopilot controls the helm at various rates or speeds. The system automatically detects the heading error, and it causes the helm to move enough in the other direction to reduce this change to zero. This system provides significant advantages, since the pilot becomes adaptable to a wider range of boats and many of the normal operator controls can become automatic. In other words, the proportional rate autopilot steers the boat in the same manner that an experienced helmsman steers, whereas the hunting and proportional deadband systems do not.

AIRCRAFT AUTOPILOTS

In airplanes, autopilots enhance safety and improve efficiency. Most airlines worldwide require jet pilots to use automatic flight control systems. While all pilots must know how to "hand-fly" (fly manually) any type of aircraft to which they are assigned, they must also undergo many hours of additional training to learn advanced automatic systems.

Airplane autopilots have a range of functions; they hold attitude and heading, track navigation signals, and free the human pilot to look for traffic, communicate with controllers, read charts, and monitor weather and air traffic control. Autopilots fly more precisely and smoothly than humans. They have a roll control and pitch control, and they can read charts, talk on the radio, call attitudes, and handle gear and flaps, all in addition to flying the plane.

In a plane, the assigned attitude (direction) is preset. When the plane moves more than 300 feet (90 m) away from the setting, the autopilot informs the pilot. As the autopilot's sensors detect errors in a flight path, a computer directs "servos," or relay devices, to move the flight controls until the error is resolved.

Some autopilot systems have control-wheel steering (CWS), a feature that allows a pilot to hand-fly without shutting off the autopilot. Once the CWS button is released, control returns smoothly to the autopilot, which maintains the attitude of the plane at the time of CWS button release. Some autopilots have pitch synchronization (PS) buttons. The PS allows the pilot to reset the attitude, and when the button is released, the autopilot follows that new setting.

Sometimes, aviation authorities recommend that autopilots not be used, such as when the plane is flying through turbulence, for example, and a human pilot's experience and reflexes are needed.

Opposite page: Above: In this simplified drawing of an autopilot system, three gyroscopes mounted on the inertial platform feed data to the computer, which in turn displays the plane's position on the Horizontal Situation Indicator. The information is used by the autopilot to correct the plane's course. Below: This diagram shows the basic elements of an autopilot system.

AIR AUTOPILOT

GYROSCOPES (top)
1 gyros mounted on an inertial platform
2 air data computer
3 amplifier
4 Horizontal Situational Display
5 autopilot controller

AIRPLANE (bottom)
1 rudder
2 rudder servo
3 elevators
4 to elevator servos
5 radio
6 computer
7 sensors
8 ailerons
9 to aileron servos
10 roll axis
11 pitch axis
12 yaw axis

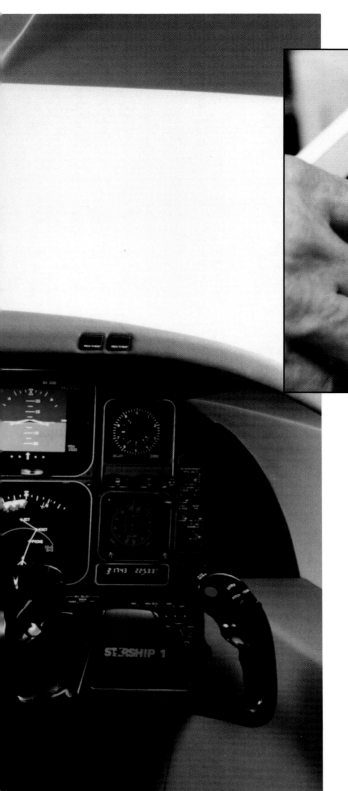

In small, private planes, the autopilot system often consists only of altitude and heading controls, with commands set by the pilot. In larger, commercial aircraft, the autopilot generally includes a navigation system that can carry out long-range, preprogrammed flight plans.

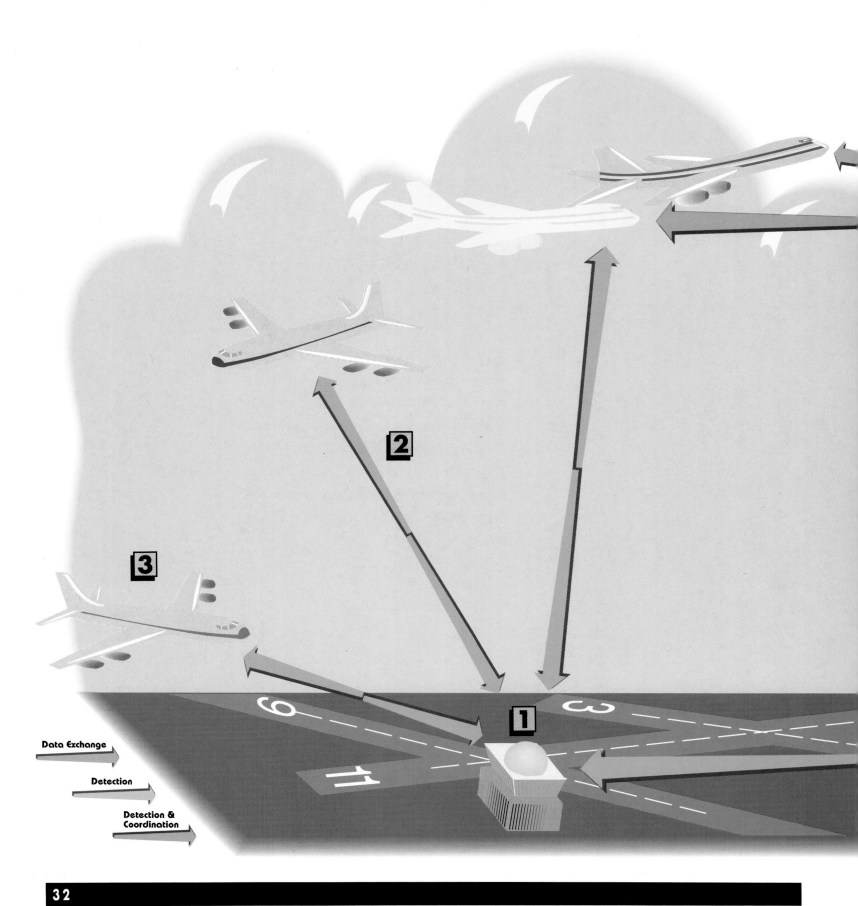

Data Exchange

Detection

Detection & Coordination

AIR TRAFFIC CONTROL

Have you ever watched the planes take off at a busy airport or seen numbers of aircraft lined up on the runway awaiting takeoff clearance, while new planes keep appearing to land? How do all those pilots know where and when to fly to keep out of each other's way?

Keeping those planes in a safe flying pattern is the job of the air traffic control radar system and the air traffic controllers, who study it second by second throughout the day and night.

The air traffic control tower functions as a radar station, emitting signals that are detected and returned by the aircraft, allowing the air traffic controllers to plot on their screens all the traffic at the airport. To further assist pilots and controllers in avoiding dangerous situations, the TCAS, or Traffic Alert and Collision-Avoidance System, uses radar signals to help planes detect each other's positions and coordinate safe movements.

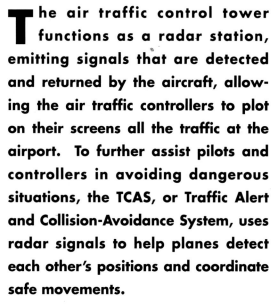

AIR TRAFFIC CONTROL

1	air traffic control tower
2	radio waves are received and returned
3	incoming aircraft
4	radar tower
5	aircraft cleared for takeoff
6	TCAS-equipped planes avoid collision

Air traffic controller Scott Sorenson in the tower overlooking Fullerton Municipal Airport in Fullerton, California. Air traffic controllers must constantly monitor their radar screens to ascertain the precise positions of the aircraft in their area.

Radar is an acronym that stands for RAdio Detection And Ranging. Radar uses radio waves to communicate between the plane and the air traffic control system.

The air traffic control tower is really a radar station, with antennas that send out radio signals. The frequencies used, however, are much higher than those used for broadcasting on your radio or television at home.

The air traffic control radar station has two radar systems, a primary one and a secondary one. Planes are also equipped with radar detectors, which are located on the underside of the belly. The radio signals from the control tower's primary radar system hit the plane's radar detector, bounce off, and return to the antenna. The information is carried by an electric signal that travels to the air traffic controller's radar screen. The length of time it takes for the signal to return to the antenna depends on the plane's distance from the tower. In this way the primary radar system tells the air traffic controller how far away the plane is.

The secondary radar system's antenna sends signals to the plane's transponders, which are located with its radar detector. The transponders send back signals that reveal the plane's identity and altitude.

The control tower antennas rotate 360 degrees, so they can locate all the planes in the air around the airport. Since it can take mere parts of a second for the signal to travel from the plane to the air traffic control system, radar stations can watch over a vast area of the sky.

The air traffic controller's radar screen displays the planes as little dim green dashes. A set of numbers follows each dash as it moves across the screen. These numbers, called a "tag," indicate the plane's altitude, the rate of descent or climb, the kind of plane (propeller or jet), and its flight number. The tags are generated and maintained in a huge computer.

The controllers can see other things on their screens, too, such as rain, snow, and developing storms, allowing the controllers to give the pilots an overall weather picture.

Collision avoidance is a major concern for all air traffic controllers. Even a momentary lapse of attention can cause the controller to miss seeing a plane that is on a collision course. That plane may be carrying 500 passengers. Since pilots cannot see all the planes around them, they rely on the air traffic controllers to be their eyes and keep them informed of any traffic in the area.

TCAS

For over 50 years, industry and government have searched for the ideal radar system. The result is the current system used in airports today, which costs several billion dollars, and is known as TCAS, which stands for Traffic Alert and Collision-Avoidance System.

There are three versions of TCAS: TCAS I, TCAS II, and TCAS III. TCAS I is a low-cost system for general aviation. It provides a "proximity alert"; that is, it advises pilots to keep alert for nearby traffic. TCAS II provides a traffic advisory, warning the pilot of the presence of another plane at a specific range, bearing, and altitude. In addition, TCAS II suggests vertical maneuvers to alleviate the problem. Planes with TCAS II equipment can detect each other and perform collision-avoidance maneuvers; therefore, TCAS II is usable in high-traffic areas near airports. TCAS III has all of TCAS II's features, but also computes horizontal collision-avoidance maneuvering.

A new radar imaging system presently under development will allow air traffic controllers to see if a plane has lowered its landing gear from a distance as great as 20 miles (32 km) away. Bernard Steinberg, the electrical engineer and University of Pennsylvania professor who developed this new system, feels that airports do not use their space efficiently—his system uses as many as 1,000 antennas placed around the airport, which send the controllers a more accurate picture of the airport traffic.

With Steinberg's method, the separate antennas function like one large antenna and send clearer images to the controllers' screens. This system would cost each airport about $5 million for the electronics alone, and the other equipment would run the cost even higher. Because of these factors, airports won't be able to use these new systems for several years.

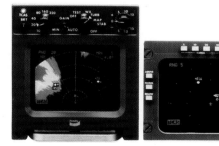

A plane euipped with TCAS can monitor the presence of all other aircraft in proximity to it. The most sophisticated system not only keeps track of the precise positions of nearby planes, it also provides data on avoiding collisions.

SPACE SHUTTLE

Prior to the space shuttle, launch vehicles for spacecraft were separate, expendable (throwaway) devices, designed for very specific, one-mission purposes. The shuttle, however, is the first reusable spacecraft (rocket system). Each shuttle has a planned operational life of 100 flights. A versatile spacecraft, it can perform a wide variety of tasks, and is the United States' only transportation system to remain in low Earth orbit (LEO), 11,000 miles (17,600 km) above the earth.

The real name of the space shuttle is the Space Transportation System (STS). The STS consists of four main parts, or subsystems: the orbiter, which is the shuttle itself; the external tank (ET); the solid rocket boosters (SRBs); and ground support.

SHUTTLE ORBITER

The orbiter is the part of the shuttle with which we are all familiar, and is the heart of the system. It is approximately the size and shape of a DC-9 commercial jet aircraft, with a length of 123 feet (37 m) and a wingspan of 78 feet (24 m). Though launched vertically like a conventional rocket, it lands horizontally like a glider; therefore, its design is much like that of an airplane.

Besides carrying a standard flight crew of three, the orbiter can accommodate up to four mission specialists, who tend up to 65,000 pounds of payload in the cargo bay.

While in orbit, the crew can launch, or deploy, a variety of experiments and hardware. Satellites can be launched, either to remain in low Earth orbit (LEO), or, through the use of auxiliary thrusters (such as the inertial upper stage [IUS]), to be boosted independently into orbits as high as geosynchronous orbit (GEO), which is 22,300 miles (35,680 km) above Earth. They can also be retrieved from orbit for repair and maintenance.

The mainframe of the 114-ton (103-metric t) vehicle is made mostly of aluminum, with titanium and advanced composites. An important difference between the orbiter and previous reentry vehicles is in the orbiter's thermal protection system (TPS). The TPS reflects heat and keeps the shuttle at a safe temperature during its reentry into the earth's atmosphere. Past insulation systems were designed to get rid of heat through melting and erosion. This process, however, destroys the object. Since the orbiter is designed to function through 100 reentries into Earth's atmosphere, a more permanent method is required.

Therefore, the orbiter's underside is covered with some 32,000 insulating tiles, which are among the most advanced heat reflectors ever invented.

The shuttle launches provided a breathtaking sight. The orbital main engines (OMEs), the most powerful rocket engines ever built, produce a thrust of 470,000 pounds (1,175,000 kg) each and an awesome mass of billowing white clouds.

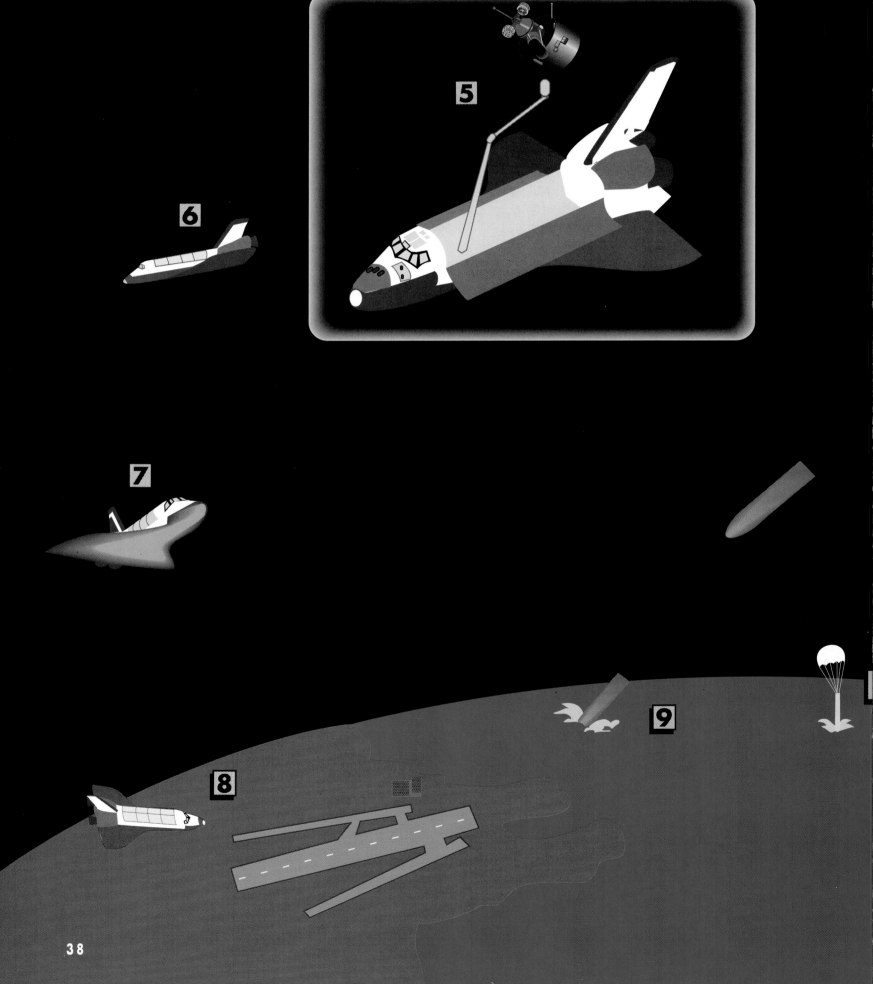

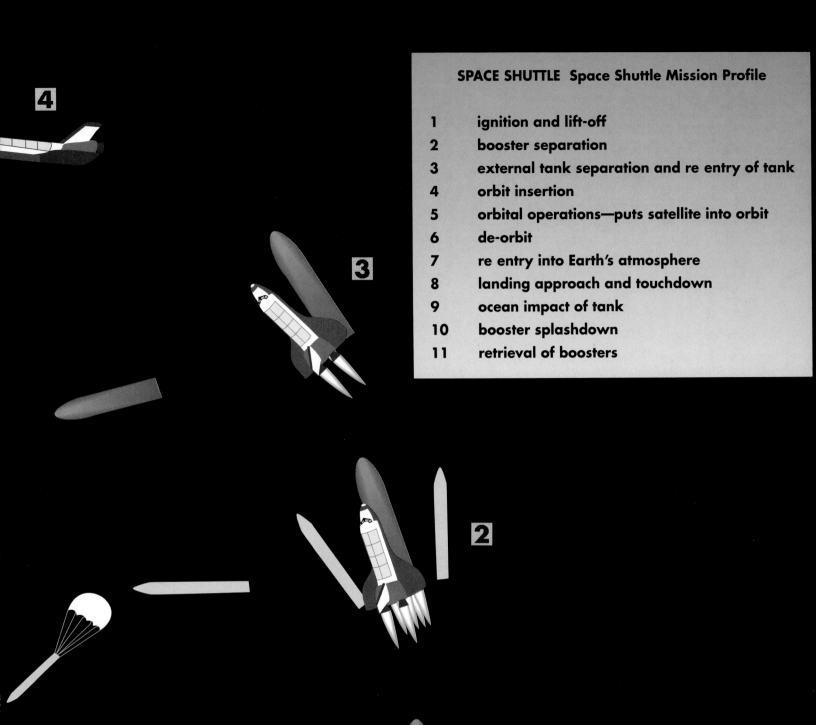

SPACE SHUTTLE Space Shuttle Mission Profile

1   ignition and lift-off
2   booster separation
3   external tank separation and re entry of tank
4   orbit insertion
5   orbital operations—puts satellite into orbit
6   de-orbit
7   re entry into Earth's atmosphere
8   landing approach and touchdown
9   ocean impact of tank
10   booster splashdown
11   retrieval of boosters

Previous page, from right to left: The space shuttle takes off from the Kennedy Spaceport like a rocket with the aid of an external fuel tank (ET) and two solid rocket boosters (SRBs). About 72 seconds into flight, the SRBs separate and fall into the ocean, where they are retrieved for refurbishment for the next space shuttle flight. Just before reaching orbit, the shuttle releases the ET, which burns up in the atmosphere. The shuttle completes its mission, then lands like a plane back at Kennedy or at Edwards Air Force Base in the Mojave Desert in California.

This fish-eye view photograph of the middeck of space shuttle *Discovery* was taken during its 5-day mission to launch the Hubble Space Telescope. In the foreground, Mission Specialist Kathryn Sullivan works with the IMAX camera, while behind her, Mission Specialist Steven Hawley consults a checklist.

The majority of the tiles are formed of silica fiber blocks covered with a glassy coating. They are attached to a layer of nylon nomex felt, which is attached to the hull with silicon adhesive. These tiles can reflect heat from a temperature range of 1,228 degrees F to 2,326 degrees F (650 degrees C to 1,260 degrees C). The tiles on the front of the wings, and those on the nosecone, wing, and tail edges, are subject to even greater temperatures—over 2,937 degrees F (1,600 degrees C). These tiles are formed of an advanced carbon composite.

The orbiter is powered by three main engines, each producing a thrust of 470,000 pounds (211,500 kg). Thrust is the driving force exerted by these engines, which operate at a temperature of 6,269 degrees F (3,515 degrees C) at a pressure of 3,000 psi (four times that of any previous rocket engine). Consuming 64,000 gallons (242,240 l) of fuel per minute, they produce a combined thrust of 1,410,000 pounds (634,500 kg).

To get into orbit and to return to Earth, the orbiter has two orbital maneuvering system (OMS) engines. Monomethyl hydrazine is the fuel; nitrogen tetroxide is the oxidizer. These ignite on contact to provide up to 6,000 pounds (2,700 kg) of thrust per engine.

For minor course corrections and attitude adjustments, the orbiter has a reaction control system (RCS) consisting of thirty-eight thrusters, each yielding 900 pounds (405 kg) of thrust, and six verniers (an extra rocket for making fine adjustments in speed or course), each providing 25 pounds (11 kg) of thrust. Fuel for the OMS and RCS is contained in tanks within the orbiter. Fuel for the main engine is carried in the external tank.

EXTERNAL TANK (ET)

In the Vertical Assembly Building at RocketDyne in Palmdale, California, the shuttle orbiter is attached to the ET. The ET is a massive structure: at 27.5 feet (8.4 m) in diameter by 155 feet (47.2 m) in length, it is half a football field long. Empty, it weighs 73,400 pounds (3,303 kg), but at lift-off it contains 1,550,000 pounds (697,500 kg) of usable propellant to feed the shuttle's main engines.

The ET is composed of three parts: a liquid oxygen (LO$_2$) tank; a liquid hydrogen (LH$_2$) tank; and an intertank section. Each of these units is a fusion-welded assembly of aluminum alloys.

The intertank is a connection piece, which receives and distributes all of the thrust loads from the solid rocket boosters and transfers these loads between the tanks. The solid rocket boosters are attached to each side of the intertank at the SRB beam, which is bolted to the thrust panels. Five ring frames form the intertank into a cylinder 22.5 feet (7 m) long.

The liquid oxygen tank consists of a diagonally ribbed nose section, a ring frame, a barrel section, and an "aft" (rear) dome section. Inside the tank is a shelflike "baffle" assembly that keeps the propellant from sloshing around.

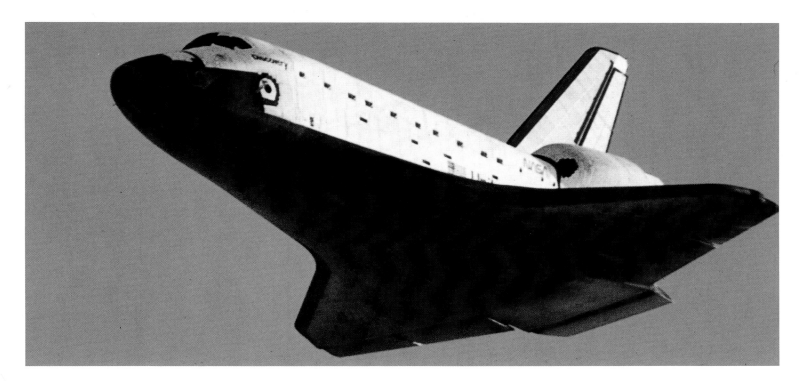

The liquid hydrogen tank consists of a forward and aft dome, four cylindrical barrel sections joined by five I-beam-shaped main ring frames. The tanks are bolted to the intertank and the assembled ET is sprayed with four types of heat-proof material and polyurethane foam insulation weighing 8,000 pounds (3,600 kg). This insulation helps to keep heat from transferring into the tanks that hold low-temperature fuels, and also helps to prevent buildup on the skin.

SOLID ROCKET BOOSTERS

The solid rocket boosters (SRBs), which measure 12 feet (3.6 m) in diameter and 149 feet (45 m) in length, are the largest solid fuel rockets ever flown. Contained within the 1/2-inch (1-cm) steel shell, and surrounded by insulation, are 1,100,000 pounds (495,000 kg) of propellant. A mixture of aluminum powder (fuel), aluminum perchlorate (oxidizer), and iron oxide (a catalyst to speed up the burning rate) is bound together into a new compound. This new compound also serves as a fuel, and ignites to produce 2,560,000 pounds (1,152,000 kg) of thrust.

GROUND SUPPORT

Over the years, NASA (the United States' National Aeronautics and Space Administration) has developed a unique, worldwide network of ground-based operations. This support system consists of design, research and development, and administration units as well as launch facilities, such as the Kennedy Space Center, where two thirds of the shuttle launches occur. Facilities of the Department of Defense are also used, such as Edwards Air Force Base, where the shuttle lands.

As the shuttle comes in for a landing, the 32,000 silica foam block tiles on its underbelly are clearly visible. These tiles have a special silicon adhesive and can reflect heat from temperatures up to 2937°F (1614°C).

In April 1984, space shuttle *Challenger* flew a mission to repair damage on the Solar Maximum Mission Satellite. After matching the satellite's orbit, Challenger performed a series of complex docking maneuvers to position the SMMS in the aft cargo bay, where it is seen in this photo, backdropped against the earth. Here, Astronaut James D. Van Hoften is seen wearing the Manned Maneuvering Unit (MMU), a nitrogen-propelled, hand-controlled backpack device that allows the wearer to move about in space.

HOW THE SHUTTLE FLIES

As mentioned before, the shuttle is launched like a rocket, standing on end. During the final countdown, the orbital maneuvering system engines and the solid rocket boosters are fired up, and these give the shuttle the push it needs to overcome Earth's gravity. Amid billowing white clouds, the shuttle rises into the air, and when it is 28 miles (45 km) up, which is about seventy-two seconds into the flight, the SRBs are separated from the orbiter and ET. Attached to parachutes, the SRBs land in the ocean, from which they are recovered, refurbished, and reused. Propelled now by its three main engines, the shuttle continues its climb with increasing speed.

Just before the shuttle reaches orbit, the ET is separated, and it falls back into the atmosphere and burns up. The orbiter continues on into orbit by itself, where it then begins to circle the earth upside down. When the mission is finished, it fires the orbital main engines again to drive it out of orbit and back through the earth's atmosphere, where it is piloted by the shuttle commander to a landing on a runway at Edwards Air Force Base in Southern California or, if conditions there are too windy, at White Sands, New Mexico.

SHUTTLE LIMITATIONS

The shuttle is an impressive piece of engineering and design, but it has certain limitations. While the launch cargo capacity is 65,000 pounds (29,250 kg), reentry capacity is less than 32,000 pounds (14,400 kg). This has been a limiting factor in the design of the European Space Agency's (ESA) *Spacelab*, which must be returned to Earth after each flight.

A maximum of four mission specialists limits the number of hands-on experiments that can be accomplished in orbit. Most importantly, however, missions are limited to no more than seven days. While mission length will expand in the future to thirty days, its present length prevents long-term experiments requiring human participation.

The orbiter's three fuel cells produce a peak power output of 36 kilowatts with an average of 14 kilowatts. They can produce a total of 1,530 kilowatt-hours of energy, which will be fully consumed in thirty days. This is the absolute limit to the mission length, even though additional food, air, and water could be economically carried for up to sixty days.

A 25-kilowatt solar power array (solar panel) could extend the mission length to the full sixty days, but even that amount of power limits such energy-dependent experiments as materials processing in space, which may require upwards of 50 kilowatts.

The shuttle is best used for the purpose for which it was designed: as a transportation vehicle. Excellent at lifting things into or returning them from orbit, its cost effectiveness and performance deteriorates when it is also expected to function as a research or manufacturing platform. Accordingly, plans are underway to build a Space Station to fulfill those needs.

As you probably already know, the space shuttle program has had many problems. For twenty-four flights, everything went smoothly, and shuttle flights became almost routine in the public mind. Then on STS-25, the ill-fated flight of the space shuttle *Challenger* in January 1986, the failure of the O-rings cost the lives of the seven-member crew. Although the flights resumed in 1989, the entire shuttle fleet was grounded again in 1990 for about six months, due to mechanical problems.

HOW THE CREWS LIVE AND WORK

Crews of five to seven astronauts live in the shuttle for up to one week. The shuttle doesn't have much room inside. Its two decks are each about the size of the interior of a camper. There isn't much privacy. The astronauts sleep in sleeping bags attached to the walls and eat freeze-dried food. The first shuttles didn't have a real toilet, but one was installed when women astronauts began to fly. The shuttle has a shower, too. It is a large plastic sack (made out of shower curtain–type plastic) that draws closed around the neck.

There is no gravity in the shuttle. The astronauts float freely inside and push off from the walls to get where they want to go. They don't have to wear space suits except during takeoff. Once they are in space, they wear jumpsuits just like those they wear on Earth.

Shuttle crews work in a shirt-sleeve environment, but that environment has no gravity.

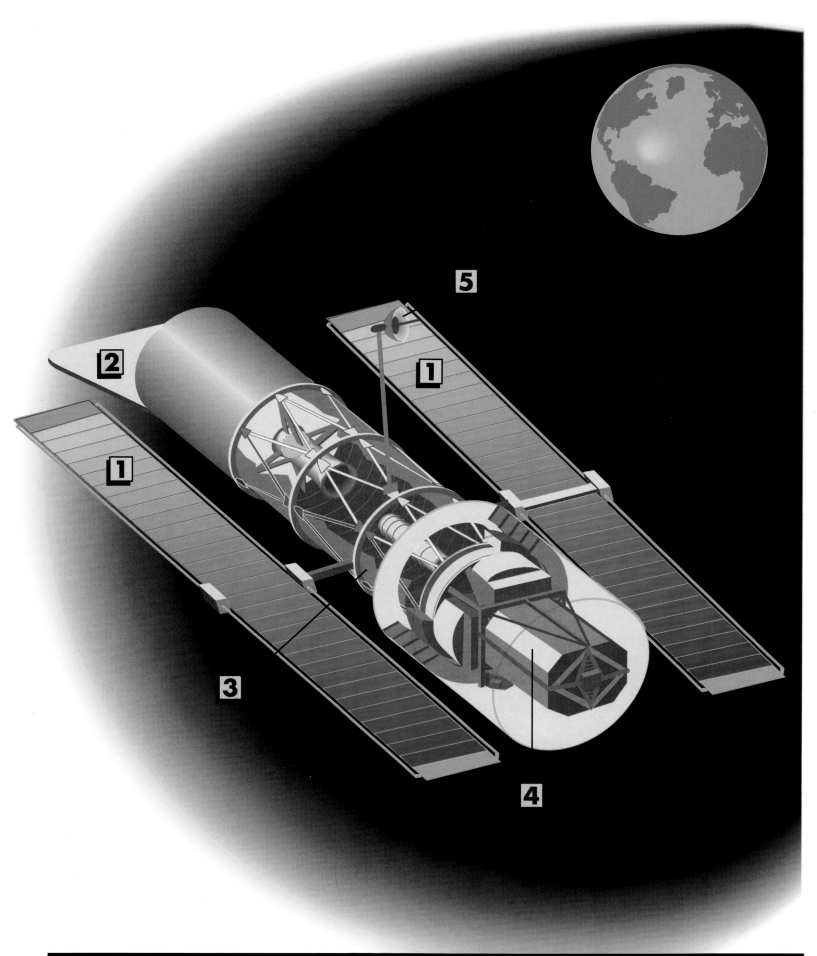

HUBBLE SPACE TELESCOPE

For years, scientists and science fiction writers alike have dreamed of having a giant telescope in space to help in solving the mysteries of the universe. Back in the early 1920s, rocket pioneer Herman Oberth spoke of the benefits of such a telescope and described his concept for what would later become the Hubble Space Telescope. In 1924, Edwin Hubble, after whom the telescope was eventually named, proved that there are other galaxies beyond our own Milky Way. After World War II, interest in building a large space telescope began to grow.

During the thirty-fifth space shuttle flight, April 25, 1990, the *Discovery* mission made that dream a reality, when it launched the Hubble Space Telescope from its cargo bay.

Why do we need a telescope in space? Because the atmosphere around the earth hinders our view from the ground; putting a telescope beyond the atmosphere means the view will be clear. In fact, the Hubble's viewing capacity is designed to be seven to ten times greater than images from Earth-based telescopes. This increased ability means the Hubble can see objects up to 14 billion light-years away. A light-year is how far light travels in a year. That means that if Hubble sees an object 14 billion light-years away, the image that it receives left its point of origin 14 billion years ago.

Orbiting 330 nautical miles (611 km) above the earth, the Hubble is expected to greatly expand our knowledge of astronomy. Not only will it be able to help determine the age of the universe by dating the most ancient stars in the centers of star clusters, but it may be able to study the light waves produced after the Big Bang.

EQUIPMENT

Part telescope and part satellite, the Hubble is a 43-foot (13-m)-long, 14-foot (4.3-m)-diameter cylinder weighing 12 tons (11 metric t), and, as such, is the largest orbiting observatory ever built. Its optical telescope assembly has three parts: an optical system, structural supports for the system, and optical control sensors. Its concave primary mirror, 94.5 inches (2.4 m) in diameter, condenses incoming light onto a 12.5-inch (30-cm) convex secondary mirror placed about 16 feet (5 m) in front of it. As radiation hits the primary mirror and reflects to the secondary mirror, it is sent back through a hole in the center of the primary mirror to form an image field.

Built at a cost of $1.5 billion, the Hubble has eight cameras, including the wide-field/planetary camera (WF/PC), a faint object camera (FOC), a high-speed photometer, some spectrographs, and some fine-guidance sensor

Orbiting 330 nautical miles (611 km) above Earth, the Hubble Space Telescope can see objects up to 14 billion lightyears away. Its view is not obstructed by our planet's atmosphere, giving the Hubble Space Telescope an enormous capacity to add to scientists' knowledge of space.

HUBBLE SPACE TELESCOPE

1	solar panels
2	aperture door
3	telescope tube
4	scientific instruments
5	transmitter

astrometers, plus a radio dish to send the data back to Earth. With this powerful light amplifier and focusing equipment, it can take pictures of stars that are twenty-five times fainter than the dimmest object visible from Earth. To accomplish this, the telescope is designed to hold so steady that its movement would be less than the thickness of a sheet of paper.

The WF/PC, or "wiff-pic," as it is called, weighs 60 pounds (27 kg) and is made up of two photometric camera systems of different focal lengths that share the same housing and electronics. With these cameras, the WF/PC can photograph images of both large amounts of space and close-up angles of planets in the solar system. The camera in the wide-field mode could cover a giant galaxy 60 million light-years away with just four exposures. It also sees the widest variety of light wavelengths, from the near

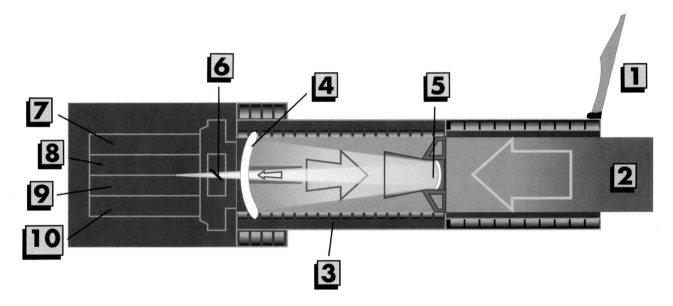

Light rays from a distant object such as a star enter the Hubble Space Telescope, bounce off the primary mirror, and are then reflected back to form an image at the focal point. The Hubble's sophisticated camera equipment captures the image and sends it back to Earth for study.

infrared to the ultraviolet. Color filters are used to help determine the structure, brightness, and composition of distant galaxies, stars, and gas clouds.

Once taken, the photographic images are broken down into hundreds of thousands of digitized picture elements, or pixels, and transmitted to the Space Telescope Operations Control Center at the Kennedy Space Center in Florida. There, the images are constructed into high-resolution photographs. Because of the Hubble's high spatial-resolution capabilities, these images are the sharpest ever sent from space.

The faint object camera is one of the four science instruments that are mounted at the back end of the Hubble. This instrument was provided by the European Space Agency (ESA) and manufactured by Dornier Systems of the Federal Republic of Germany, British Aerospace, and Matra, of Italy. The faint object camera will be used to study binary and supergiant stars, black holes believed to exist at the center of galaxies, and the activity of quasars and radio galaxies. Although it can't photograph as wide an expanse of space as the WF/PC, it will see farther into the universe than any other instrument. It has the ability to intensify distant images up to 100,000 times their original brightness.

The Hubble will also observe gaseous nebulae and will monitor atmospheric and surface phenomena of the planets in Earth's solar system, and look for the presence of planets around other stars. One of the most interesting things the Hubble was designed to do was to help determine the age of the universe by dating the oldest stars within star clusters.

THE HUBBLE IN ACTION

After launch, the Hubble's main power buses were activated, and initial communications were established. Then began a ninety-day orbital verification period to check all systems.

NASA engineers had hoped to take the first picture about a week after the telescope was launched, but instead had to struggle to align and focus the instruments, as well as to correct computer problems, a fouled antenna, and a programming error that resulted from a simple math miscalculation.

To make matters worse, it was rapidly discovered that the mirrors on the space telescope were flawed and could not perform properly. The problem was twofold: Perkin-Elmer, the manufacturer of the mirrors, had given the subcontractors backward drawings for part of the telescope's guidance system. This means that where Hubble had been expected to focus on 70 percent of starlight energy within a 0.2 arc second wide area, it can only focus on 10 to 25 percent. The flaw consists of a 2-micron error in the prescription of the shape of one of the mirrors. According to Leonard Fisk, NASA associate administrator for space science, this is the same as a difference of one-fiftieth of the diameter of a human hair.

The real tragedy is that this problem could have been avoided had the proper tests been run while Hubble was on the ground. The Air Force had offered Perkin-Elmer the equipment to perform the necessary tests, but NASA refused to accept the offer because it felt that the tests were technically unnecessary. Perkin-Elmer also refused because in order to take advantage of the Air Force's offer, all of their employees had to have secret clearances, which they did not. In addition, the company felt it would add hundreds of millions of dollars to the cost of the telescope. So the tests went unrun and the design flaw was not discovered until Hubble was already in space.

How are these problems going to be resolved? In 1992 or 1993, a shuttle mission will replace the WF/PC. Many of the parts already exist at the Jet Propulsion Laboratory in Pasadena, California, and so a new camera will be assembled. Eight new mirrors will be needed, however, for each of the eight cameras to correct the focus problem with the primary telescope.

NASA has reorganized the schedule of the programs that were to run on Hubble. A number of the observing programs that will be performed over the next few years can proceed as planned, since they use the tele-

HUBBLE SPACE TELESCOPE

1	aperture door
2	light rays from star or galaxy
3	stray-light baffles
4	primary mirror
5	secondary mirror
6	pick-off mirror for wide field/planetary camera
7	faint-object camera
8	high resolution spectrograph
9	faint-object spectrograph
10	high-speed photometer

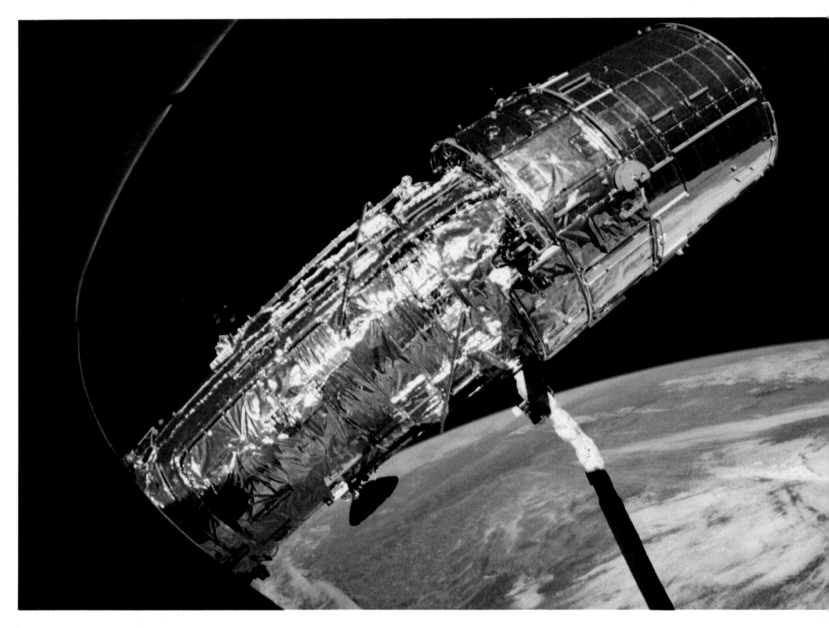

The Hubble Space Telescope reflected in one of the space shuttle *Discovery's* mirrors as it is deployed into space.

scope's other capabilities. Other programs will run earlier, to check out all systems. NASA is attempting to utilize the Hubble in its current state, trying to use the spectrographs to assess components of the primordial gas out of which galaxies form and seeing if computer enhancement can improve the quality of the images.

The FOC also has problems. It can do work in ultraviolet, but not in the visual mode, where scientists had hoped it would take pictures of stars five to seven times farther away than any ground-based telescope can see. A replacement can be sent in 1996, but since Hubble has a life span of only fifteen years, much time has been lost.

Despite these problems, the Hubble has transmitted some fascinating data. On May 20, 1990, the Hubble successfully collected information about Theta Carina, a Milky Way star cluster located about 1,260 light-years from Earth.

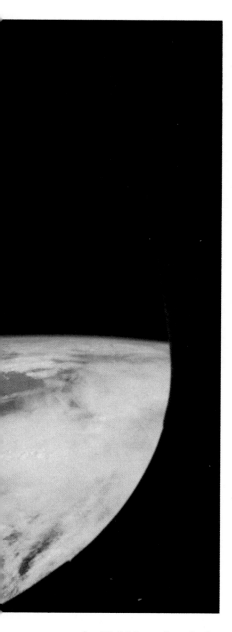

As Hubble orbited above Jayapura, New Guinea, the shutter of its WF/PC opened for one second to take the first black-and-white picture. That photo, and a second exposure lasting thirty seconds, were stored on magnetic tape and relayed to the ground.

Engineers took more than an hour to change the raw electronic data into a properly contrasting picture on a TV screen. The thirty-second exposure revealed dozens of stars in a star cluster. This cluster is so large that, to the naked eye from Earth, it appears twice as wide as the moon.

Comparing those photos to ground-based ones, NASA scientists thought it on target and in better focus than anticipated. What had previously been believed to be one star was now revealed to be two stars.

Although it may not perform as well as anticipated, it is clear that the Hubble will penetrate far deeper into the mysteries of the universe than humans have ever looked before.

The Hubble Space Telescope is seen suspended in space by *Discovery's* Remote Manipulator System prior to the deployment of its solar panels and antennae and its ultimate release. The land masses visible on the earth at the left of the photo are Puerto Rico and the Dominican Republic. This photograph was taken with a hand-held Hasselblad camera.

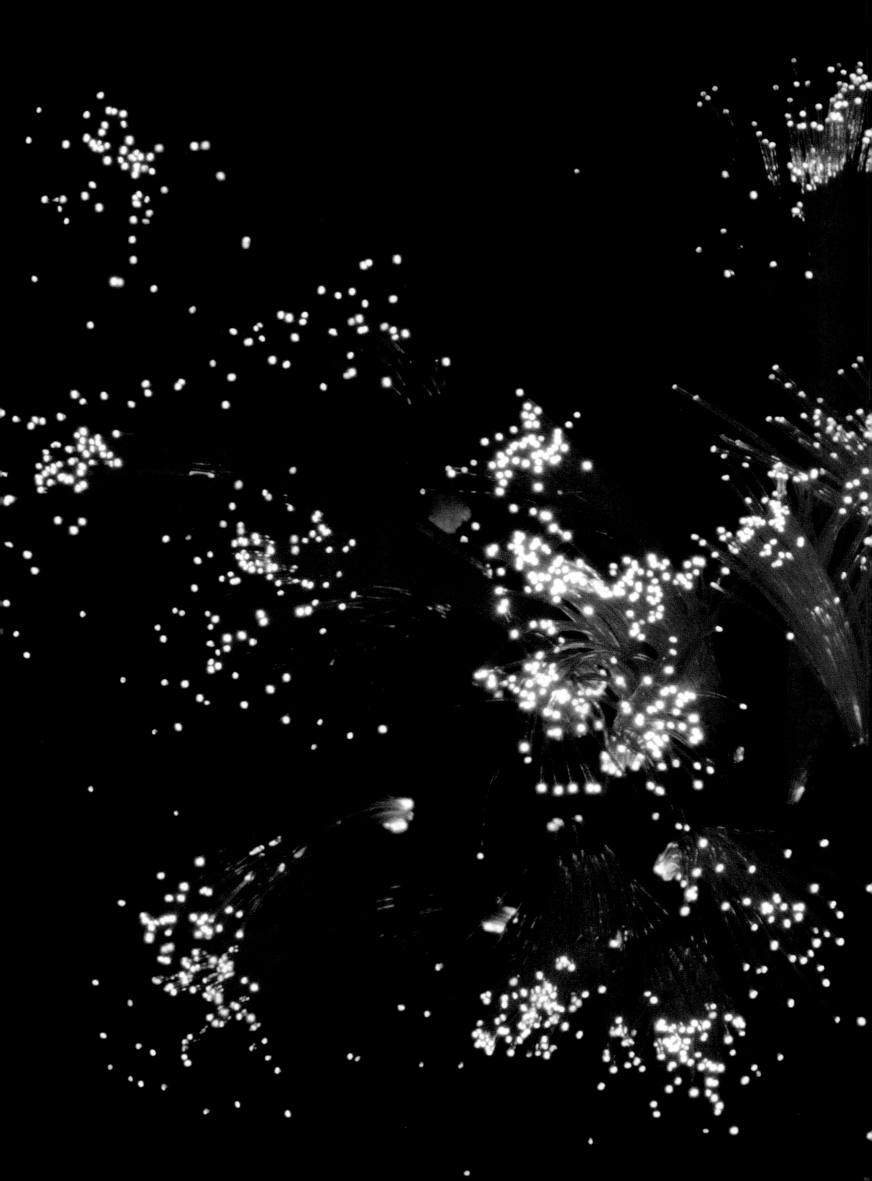

PART TWO
COMMUNICATIONS TECHNOLOGY

TAPE RECORDER

The tape recorder is a commonly used device in modern life, from the large reel-to-reel machines used in recording studios through cassette recorders in stereos, to small handheld recorders that either use standard (mini) cassettes or microcassettes. You may think the technology is new, but tape-recording technology was actually developed in the 1930s.

RECORD AND PLAYBACK

The basic process of tape recording is that the recorder translates sound waves into electrical impulses, stores them on magnetic tape, then turns the impulses back into sound waves when the tape is played. How does the tape hold sound? Recording tape is made of a thin polyester backing evenly coated on one side with very fine particles of an iron oxide compound, which is most commonly chromium dioxide or a non-alloy. These particles line up in nice, neat rows. The coatings are "ferromagnetic"; that means they can be magnetized.

Sounds are converted into electrical impulses when the microphone picks up the sound, and the diaphragm inside the microphone starts to vibrate. Very thin wires pick up the vibrations and convert them into voltage bursts, then transmit those into the recorder. The voltage flows to the recording head, which is a small C-shaped electromagnet about the size of a quarter. The tape, with its particles arranged like tiny bar magnets with north and south poles, moves through the mechanism, and is magnetized.

When the magnetized sound hits the nice, neat rows of particles, the affected particles rearrange into a jumbled pattern that represents (characterizes) the sound received. The variations in voltage become the same variations in magnetization. The sound is now stored on the tape. This type of recording is known as "analog," because the recording takes a form that is analogous to, or representative of, the original sound.

What happens when we play the tape? The jumbled pattern of magnetic particles moves through the magnetic playback head and produces electric signals, which travel to an amplifier, which then carries the sound to a set of speakers. The speakers translate the sound back into its original form.

Most tape recorders can also erase the sounds on a tape. They erase with an erasing head, which takes the jumbled particles and reorganizes them back into nice, neat rows containing no sound at all.

Previous page: As the tape moves from the feed spool into the tape recorder, the tape guide wheel regulates the speed at which the spool rotates. If the erase button on the machine is pushed, a magnetic field is produced from the erase head, which disorients the magnetic particles on the tape, erasing any data previously stored there. The record button brings the magnetized record head into contact with the tape, magnetizing the particles so that they represent the sounds being recorded. Pressing the play button activates the replay head. The pressure pad (located in the cassette tape) pushes the tape against the replay head. When the magnetized replay head comes into contact with the magnetic particles on the tape, electrical signals are produced, which travel to the amplifier and then to the speakers.

THE STATE OF ANALOG RECORDING

Analog tape recording has its problems, however. A lot of energy is needed to reorganize the particles, and this can create severe distortion of the sound at low signal levels. To remedy this problem, most modern recorders mix an ultrasonic sound, called bias, with the voltage received. Bias usually occurs at high frequencies (around 100 kHz) and therefore cannot be heard by the human ear. Bias keeps the recording head out of the low frequencies. The amount of bias used differs with each type of tape, so most recorders use what are called bias trimmers to adjust for it.

Another problem with magnetic tape is that it can only become magnetized a limited number of times; in other words, it eventually loses its ability to hold and/or play sound. Have you ever played a tape and just gotten a lot of distortion while the recorded sound is muffled in the background? This phenomenon is called tape saturation.

The tape can also lose its magnetization at high frequencies, resulting in blank spots on the tape. This problem is called self-erasure. Playback equalization is a feature that helps regulate the quality of the sound.

Hiss may also be encountered with analog tape, so noise reduction systems are very important. The standard for cassette noise reduction are Dolby B circuits, invented by the same company that puts Dolby stereo sound on many movies.

Left: The amplifier increases the voltage of the electrical signals produced by the tape recorder, then sends the signals to the speakers, which reproduce them as sound.

Below: In analog recording (bottom), the tape stores the sound information as a continuous stream of magnetized particles formed into longitudinal tracks. Digital tape (top) stores the sound signals as precise sequences of magnetism.

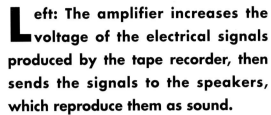

TAPE RECORDER

1   digital tape
2   analog tape

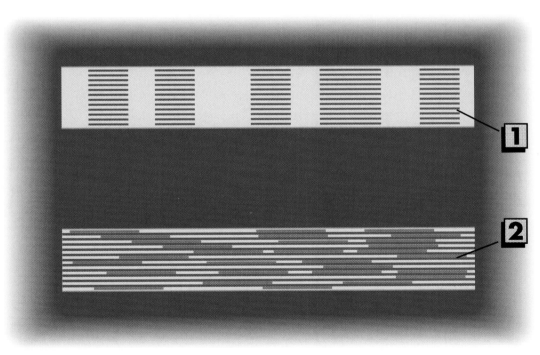

DIGITAL AUDIO TAPE

Just about everything these days seems to be "digital," from digital clocks to digital scales and now digital audio tape (DAT)—but what does digital mean? The term originated among computer programmers, who used it to describe information that is presented in the form of on-off binary digits. The simplest way to represent these digits is as a series of ones and zeros. These digits can be used to code many different kinds of information.

When we talked about analog recording we mentioned that the sound information was recorded in a way that is analogous to the incoming signal. Digital recording is a different process that represents a major advance in how sound is recorded. Digital audio tape (DAT) is what is called a helical (spiral) scan recording technology. That means the recording head rotates rapidly as the tape moves across it, so much more sound is packed onto a smaller tape (only one-fifth of an inch, or 4 mm, wide) than with traditional static-head recording devices. DAT keeps recording speed down to about one-third of an inch, or 8.15 mm, per second, which makes the tape last much longer.

Helical-scan recording has been around even longer than flexible disk, cartridge, and reel-to-reel drives. This technology was originally developed to effectively record television signals on slow-moving tape.

SAMPLING

Based on home video recording technology (see page 58), digital audio tape samples the incoming signal electronically. That means a processing microchip slices the sound wave information into small periods of time. These slices of time are called samples. Each sample is then translated into binary digits, or bits. (Bits are the on-off binary codes used by computer programmers that were defined above.)

Some of the bits represent volume (amplitude), while others represent pitch (frequency). Once the samples are translated into bits, they can be encoded onto the tape in a rapid high-low sequence of magnetism. Digital recording uses complicated sixteen-bit codes, used to sample more than 65,000 levels of voltage at a rate of more than 40,000 times per second. The resulting samples are extremely accurate.

Although digital recording preserves the voltage of the sound the microphone produces just as analog recording does, the digital version's accuracy is far greater. In addition, while analog recording requires noise-reduction systems to reduce the background hiss, digital recording is free from this noise. Consequently, digital recordings reproduce copies that are very close to the master recording.

When a DAT tape is played back, the recorder translates each sample into sound, then links the samples together to re-create the music. You will never hear the pauses between samples, just as you don't see the gaps between movie frames. They both move too fast.

MARKETING DAT

A great deal of controversy has surrounded DAT. Attempts have been made to stop the marketing of DAT to avoid competition with less advanced systems, and manufacturers promised not to talk publicly about DAT. The president of Phillips, Cor Van Der Klugt, said that the time was not right for introducing this new format. He felt buyers would only be confused by the addition of DAT tapes to records, CDs, and analog cassettes.

Another fear was that marketing DAT at that time would risk the market for the CD technology, which was just gaining a foothold. The underlying concern, however, was that CD manufacturers were worried about copyright infringement. CDs can only play back, while digital audio tape can both playback and record. In addition, DAT sound quality is even better.

Eighty-five manufacturers have designed DATS that cannot copy CDs digitally, but experts warn that copying is still possible and that the sound quality is exceptionally good. Manufacturers fear that a CD/DAT player combination product would allow pirating operations to sprout up everywhere. Illegal copying already costs manufacturers over $350 million every year. DAT, they believe, could make the pirating much worse. Furthermore, DATs are cheaper than CDs.

Critics, however, remind manufacturers to take a lesson from history: Moviemakers succeeded in stalling pay television from the 1940s, when Zenith first came out with a pay-TV system, until the 1970s, when it finally became available to the public. Similarly, they fought the introduction of the VCR just as hard. In the end, both cable and the VCR succeeded in creating new markets for movies that would not have been big box-office hits in the theaters. These critics argue that DATs will be cheap enough that people will not feel the need to pirate them.

Even though DATs remain controversial at the moment, it seems inevitable that it is only a matter of time before they reach the home market. There is a new international agreement based on a system called the serial copying management system (SCMS). It contains an electronic circuit that allows duplication of copyrighted material, but will not make copies from DATs. Developed by Phillips, the SCMS reads a copyright flag from the inaudible subcode channel on CDs or other sources. The DAT is programmed not to record from that source.

The digital audio tape player operates like a video recorder, using a rapidly rotating replay/record head that allows it to store more information more accurately than an analog recorder.

In helical scan recording, the video-tape wraps around the rotating drum at an angle, resulting in the video tracks being laid down diagonally, as in this close-up diagram of a video tape. The sound signals are recorded along the top of the tape and the synchronization, or control signals, which control the picture, are recorded along the bottom.

VCR TAPE

1   audio tracks

2   video tracks

3   control signals

VIDEO CASSETTE RECORDER

In the days before videocassette recorders (VCRs), you had to be home to watch when a favorite show came on. VCRs have liberated us from adhering to the networks' programming schedules. Now, you can watch when *you* have the time. Recording shows for later viewing is the most common use for VCRs, and is called "time shifting."

VCRs come in two basic types: VHS (video home system) and Beta. Just like DAT recorders, these VCRs use a rapidly rotating cylinder head to "helically" scan a slow-moving magnetic tape. Both offer features such as a remote control, fourteen-to-twenty-one-day programming (so you can record while you are on vacation), a clock, freeze frame, pause, frame advance, slow motion, and dubbing.

The two formats are not compatible, however; you cannot use a Beta cassette in a VHS machine or a VHS cassette in a Beta machine. The Beta cassette is smaller and, when played at slower speeds, has a slightly superior picture. Because VHS has a longer playing and recording time (six hours versus Beta's five), it has become the more popular format. Sony has a Beta with a "Beta stack" that holds four tapes and provides twenty hours of recording—a feature that VHS does not share.

Most VHS models record and play at three speeds: SP (standard play, two hours); LP (long play, four hours); and EP (extended play, six hours). The only problem with recording at the slower speeds is that the picture is less clear than at faster speeds.

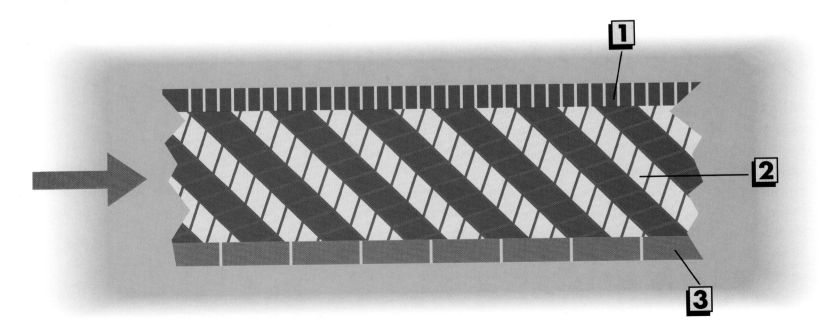

Each VHS format tape can record up to 6 hours of programming.

RECORDING

Recording electronically, VHS and Beta VCRs work in the same way. Like a television, the VCR picks up the video signal (that is, the picture) from the signal coming into the home from the television station. This signal may be either broadcast or cabled in. Instead of displaying the signal on the screen in the form of a picture, however, the VCR sends it to tape, where it is recorded in the same way a tape recorder records a sound signal.

If you look at the back of a videocassette, you will notice that a plastic trapdoor covers the tape. When the cassette is loaded into the VCR, this trapdoor is raised, exposing the tape. Inside the VCR are loading poles that move the tape from the cassette so it comes in contact with the recorder's heads and rollers.

The record/replay head rotates at a high speed as the tape passes it, storing the information from the television signal in diagonal tracks across the tape (as opposed to the horizontal tracks made by a sound tape recorder). The sound and synchronization information is stored by the audio and control head in horizontal tracks along the upper and lower edges of the tape.

With modern video technology, tapes shot using hand-held video cameras can be shown on television with a VCR.

PLAYBACK

During playback, the VCR transmits the information to the television set in the form of electric signals. The television's detectors separate the video information from the sound and synchronization information, with the former creating the picture, and the latter emerging from the speakers as sound.

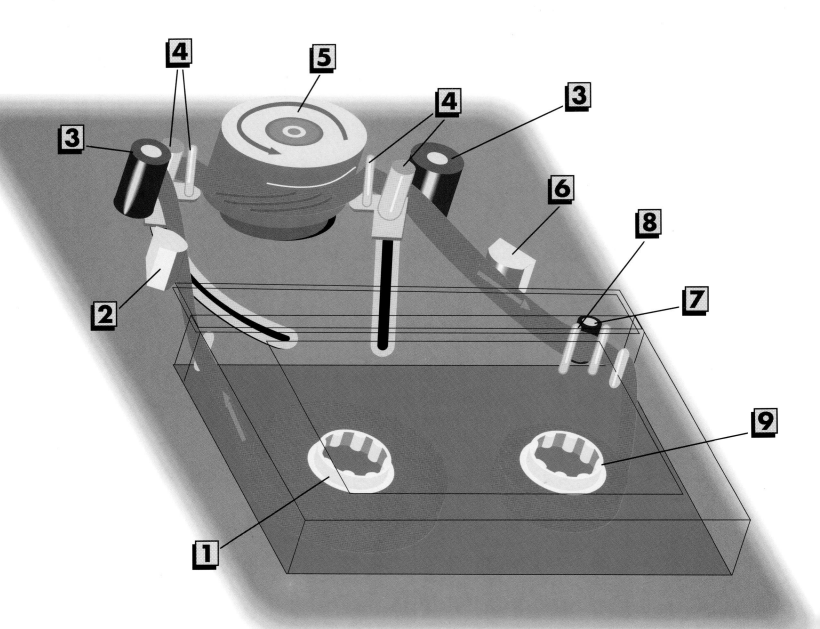

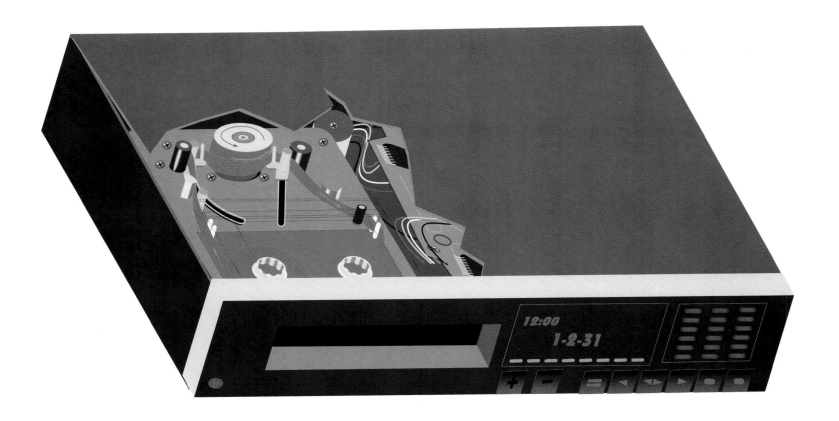

VIDEO CASSETTE RECORDER

1	feed spool
2	erase head
3	tape tension regulators
4	tape guides
5	video drum head
6	audio head
7	pinch roller
8	capstan
9	take-up spool

In a VHS recorder, the videotape follows an M-shaped path. The tape is pulled from the feed spool out of the cassette into the recorder, where it wraps around the erase head, the video drum head, and the audio head. The tape guides and tension regulators guide and maintain correct tension as the tape moves in its M-loop. The pinch roller pushes the tape against the rotating capstan, which pulls the tape back onto the take-up spool in the cassette.

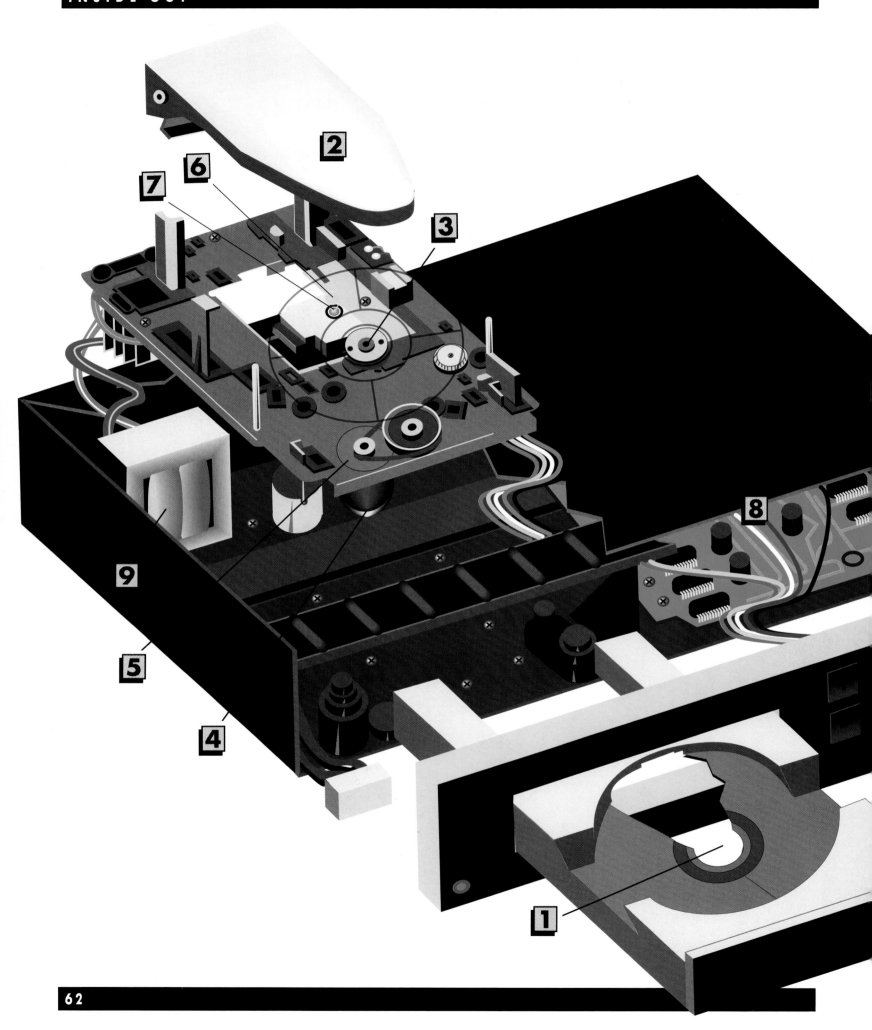

COMPACT DISC PLAYER

Have you been into a music store lately and noticed anything missing? You won't see many LP or 45 records. Most music is now found on compact discs (CDs). Records are fast becoming part of the past—your old records may soon be considered collectibles.

CDs, which are only 4.75 inches (12 cm) across and weigh a half ounce (14 g), are very different from old-fashioned records. They are made of plastic covered with a thin layer of metallic film. CDs use digital recording to etch this film with billions of tiny indentations called pits. The pits represent the sound information coded into binary on-off sequences. On an audiotape, the codes organize magnetic particles into patterns. On a CD, the codes are etched into the disc by a laser beam, forming a pitted surface. The pits form a microscopically thin, three-mile (5-km) long track on the disc.

When you play a CD, the player aims a low-powered laser light beam at the track of pits. As the CD turns inside the player, the laser light hits the pits and is reflected off the metallic film. This reflected light flickers according to the sequence of the pits, and electronic circuits translate the sequence of pulses into sound. Just as with other types of digital recordings, the quality of the sound produced is superior to that of an analog recording.

While CD players cannot play your old records, of course, they can be hooked up to your existing speakers and other components. CDs are easier to use than records, as well. For example, when you wish to move to another track on a record, you have to lift the tone arm and very carefully set it down in the blank space before the track of the song you wish to hear. One wrong move and the needle can skid across the grooves, scratching them permanently and causing the record to skip when the needle hits the scratch. With cassettes, you have to fast-forward or rewind to get to another track.

To change tracks on a CD, however, all you need do is push a button. The CD goes to the requested track in less than a second, and displays the track number. Not only that, you can program the machine to play the songs in any order or to repeat your favorite song over and over as many times as you wish.

CDs are virtually indestructible. They will last for up to a decade, and maybe longer, because nothing ever touches their surface. They can hold up to 74 minutes of sound, where a long-playing record can hold only 45. The laser light in a CD player lasts much longer than an old-fashioned record player needle, and CDs aren't as sensitive to movement, either.

The real advantage of CDs is that all CD players are built to one standard, so that any CD will work in any CD player. The disadvantage is that so far CDs are "read-only," which means that you can play them, but not record on them. This may change in the not too-distant future.

A system of mirrors and lenses is used to emit a beam of laser light and direct it to the disc, where it strikes the pits and flats that represent the disc's data. When the beam hits a flat, light is reflected back; when it strikes a pit, almost no light is reflected. The patterns of light are reflected to the photodiode, which produces electrical signals.

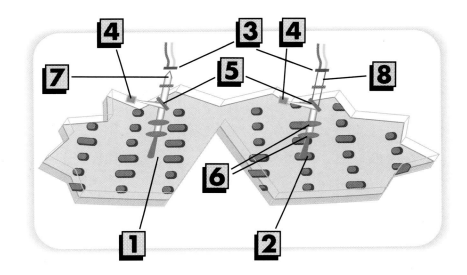

HOW A COMPACT DISC IS READ

1	flat
2	pit
3	photodiode
4	laser
5	semi-transparent mirror
6	lens
7	light is reflected
8	no light is reflected

When the platter containing the disc slides into the CD player, the flapper holds the disc in place while the spindle rotates it clockwise. A laser beam scans the disc from below, moving from the inner to the outer edge. Light that is reflected back from the disc passes to a photodiode, which converts the differences in light to varying electrical voltages. The electronic circuitry converts the signals from digital to analog format, then sends them to the amplifier and on to the speakers.

Although the compact disc appears to be a smooth surface, it actually contains a spiral track made up of many microscopic pits and flats.

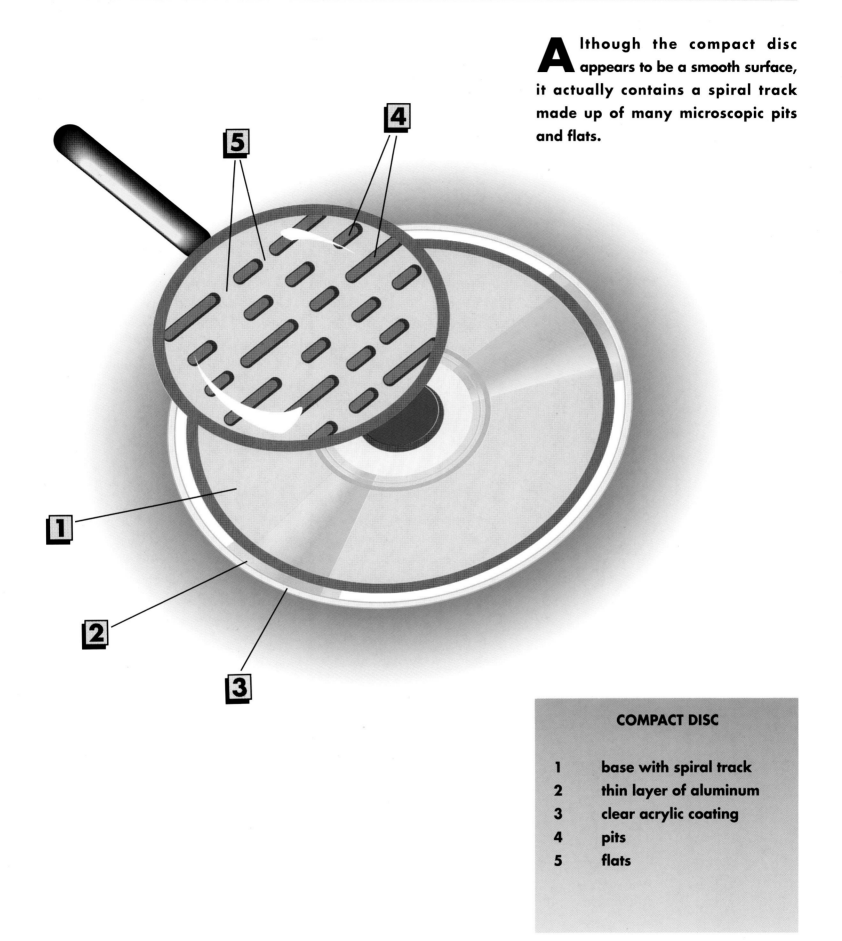

COMPACT DISC

1   base with spiral track
2   thin layer of aluminum
3   clear acrylic coating
4   pits
5   flats

FAX MACHINE

No longer is it necessary to rely on the mail or pay high prices for express delivery to get correspondence to its destination. Now, thanks to facsimile, or fax, machines, documents can reach any destination in the world in seconds.

Found in almost every office, and becoming more popular for homes, too, fax machines electronically scan a document, convert it to a digital format, then send the information over the phone lines via modem to its destination. There, the information is reproduced in a facsimile, or copy, of the original document. Billed at telephone rates, this form of transmission is even cheaper than a phone call, since the sender and receiver do not spend extra minutes in idle chitchat.

Many fax machines have built-in phones. Others are hooked up to separate phones. Some type of phone hookup is necessary because the fax machine relies on telephone lines to make contact with other fax machines. To fax, it is necessary to dial a fax machine's phone number. When the connection is made, the fax begins scanning the document.

SENDING A FAX

The document that is being sent is inserted into a slot in the fax machine. Fax machines scan documents in one of two ways: The first uses a charge-coupled device (CCD), which relies on mirrors to bounce the illuminated image into a lens where the CCD can read the information in the form of light and dark images. The second uses a contact imaging scanner (CIS). The document passes through a strip of LED (light-emission diode) displays. The LEDs reflect pixels (light and dark picture elements) of light, which are detected by a lens or fiber-optic link. This fiber-optic link is connected to electronic sensing circuits. The more compact CIS systems are more expensive than CCD ones.

From this point, both types of machines operate in the same way. The CCD or electronic circuits convert the pixels into an electric signal. This electric signal represents the shades of gray (dark and light) in the transmitted document. Some fax machines can only transmit eight shades of gray, while others can transmit as many as 64. The more shades of gray the fax can transmit, the better the quality of the picture.

Inside fax machines are rolls of paper on which the transmissions are reproduced. Some use thermal paper, which is shiny, while others use standard copy paper. The fax machine receiving the transmission uses a stylus to burn the images onto the paper. The receiver then has to cut it into pages.

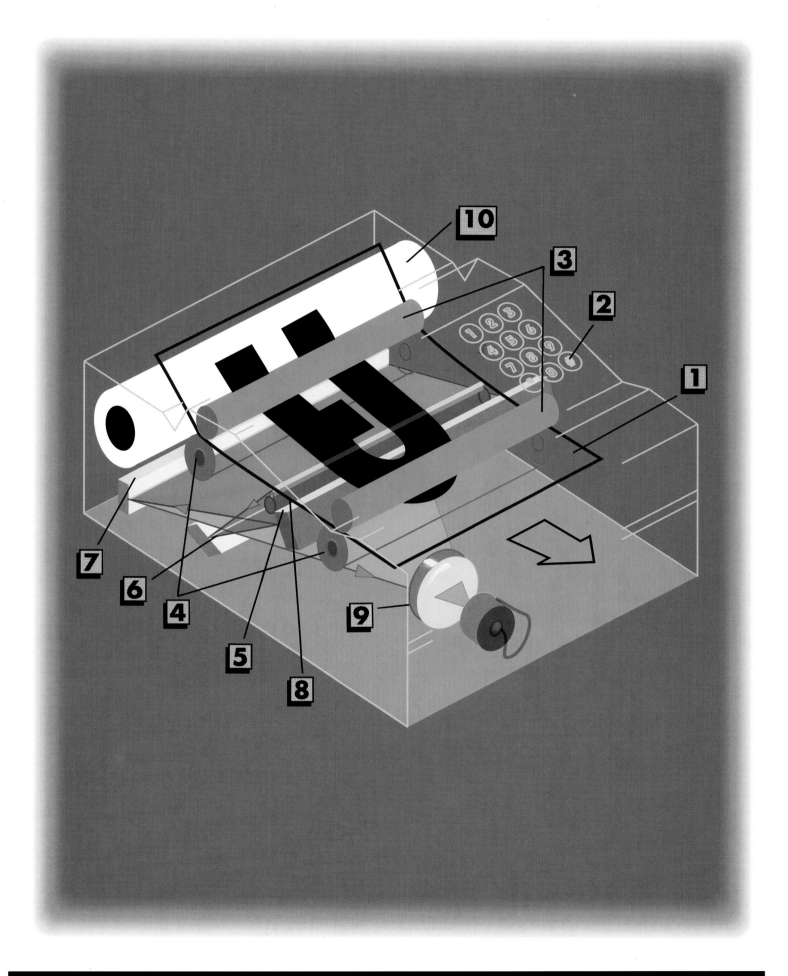

Previous page: When a document is sent using a CCD fax, a fluorescent tube illuminates the sheet of paper. An arrangement of mirrors picks up the image of the paper and reflects it into a lens, then onto the surface of the CCD. Electronic photodiodes scan the CCD, "reading," in very thin horizontal lines, the light and dark elements of the image reflected there. (Each spot detected by the photodiodes is called a picture element, or pixel.) The scanned pixels are converted into electronic signals and transmitted through the phone lines to the receiving fax machine.

Right: The CIS machine uses a row of LEDs that stretches across the document. The light from the LEDs is reflected by a single mirror into a fiber-optic link that carries the light to the electronic light-detector circuits. Because the CIS uses only one mirror and fiber-optic cable, CIS machines are smaller than CCDs.

The big advantage of fax machines over equipment such as telex machines is that they require no keyboarding. Fax machines come in both analog and digital models. Analog fax machines have four speeds, which require from two to six minutes to transmit a page. Digital models use modem speeds ranging from 2,400 bps (bits per second) to 9,600 bps. Digital fax machines can transmit a page in 12 seconds.

Fax machines were developed to a single standard, so that there is no problem with one fax machine talking to another, even though more advanced models have been developed since the first model was introduced in 1968. Those noisy, slow machines are no longer in use. The next group of machines came out in 1976, and transmit at 2,400 to 7,200 bps; these also are no longer sold. Group III machines are the current standard. They transmit at 9,600 bps, and can communicate with Group II machines. Group IV machines are on the horizon, though no standards have been developed for them as yet. They will transmit as fast as three seconds per page.

Computers with modems can also be used as fax machines. Fax boards, which are small, printed circuit boards, fit into the computer, allowing the user to fax any document in the computer. While at the present time, the transmission must be received by a fax machine, the day isn't far off when we will be able to transmit faxes from computer to computer.

Some fax machines can also act as copy machines—essentially, they send a fax to themselves—and have built-in answering machines. One model of fax machine has a clear glass top like a copy machine, which is ideal for transmitting pages from books or magazines.

A less helpful offshoot of fax technology is "junk" fax. Like junk mail, this is a transmission that the receiver has not requested, usually an advertisement or offering. The result of such unauthorized use of fax machines is likely to be subject to legislation to prevent unwanted transmissions.

CIS FAX	
1	document
2	sensor drive board
3	image sensor board
4	LED array
5	lens or fiber-optic link
6	guide
7	read roller

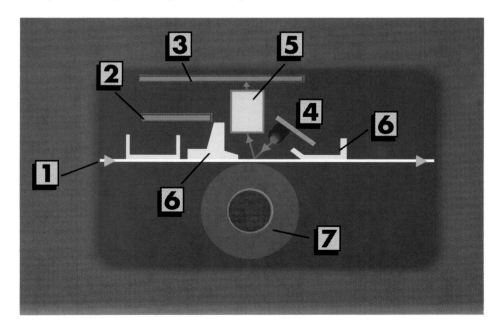

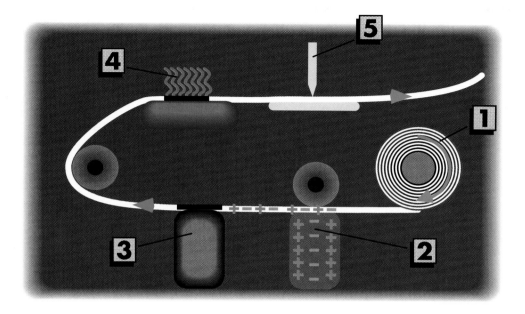

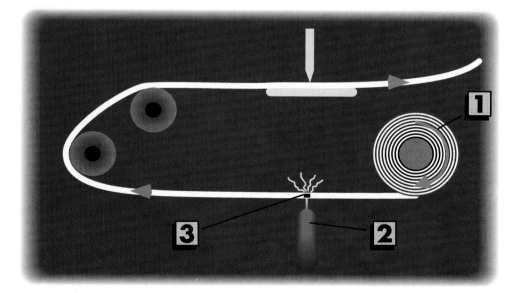

When a fax machine is receiving a document, it converts electrical signals into a copy of the original document. The thermal recording system (bottom) uses a set of fine wires positioned across the recording paper that produce hot spots as current passes through them, burning the image into the paper. In electrostatic recording (top), a charge is applied on the recording paper where a mark is needed. Black-powder toner sticks to the charged spots, which are either fused to the paper with heat or pressed onto it by rollers.

FAX MACHINE

ELECTROSTATIC RECORDING (top)		THERMAL RECORDING (bottom)	
1	paper roll	1	paper roll
2	printer head applies charge	2	photodiodes
3	toner	3	thermal recorder
4	heater		
5	cutter		

CELLULAR TELEPHONE

Cellular telephones use radio frequencies to carry their signals, unlike traditional ground based telephones, which use fiber-optic cables to carry electronic signals. They may be car phones, as pictured here, or may be hand-held or briefcase based portables.

Cellular phones, also called mobile phones, are entirely different from regular telephones. Not connected to any cables or wires, they seem to work by magic. The explanation lies in radio waves.

CELLS

Geographical areas are broken up into a grid of hexagons, or cells, a few miles or kilometers wide. Each cell contains a low-powered radio transmitter and control equipment located in a building called a "cell site."

The cell site is connected by wireline facilities to a mobile telephone switching office (MTSO), which is in turn connected to the regular telephone network through the telephone central office. The MTSO has an

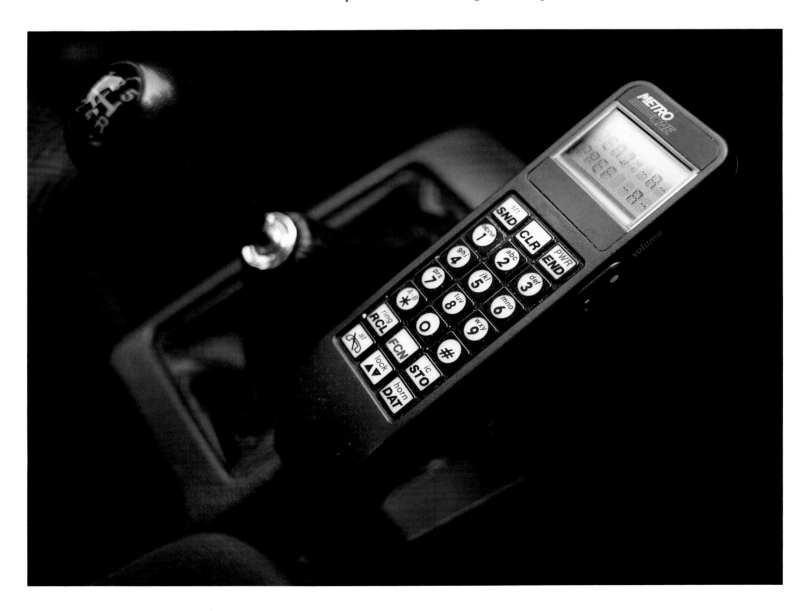

electronic switching capability, and it monitors the cars as they cross each cell.

When a car with a cellular phone passes through a cell, it eventually will reach a distance at which that cell's signal is no longer strong enough to maintain the connection. The cells overlap somewhat, however, so the connection can be "handed off" to the transmitter in the cell into which the car is headed. Thus, as the car passes into the adjoining cell, the MTSO automatically switches the conversation in progress to the next cell site's transmitter.

Each cell uses a set of radio frequencies, and several cell sites can use the same frequencies for different conversations at the same time, as long as the cells are not adjacent. Cells using the same frequencies are far enough away from one another that the signal from one cell site to a vehicle in its area will override the same signal originating farther away. That's because cellular phones use FM (frequency modulation) transmission, which produces the capture effect—meaning that the stronger signal completely overrides the weaker one, so the receiver receives the stronger signal only, and does not hear the weaker one at all.

As the transmission is handed off, the mobile phone has to switch to the frequencies of the new cell site. The cell site knows which frequencies are available and tells the phone which channel to use. This happens with only a split second of interruption.

While cellular phones save a great deal of time by allowing an efficient use of otherwise wasted commuting time, the cost of using a cellular phone is almost four times as high per minute as the cost of a regular phone call. Not only that, you also have to pay when someone calls you. As a result, about two-thirds of the cellular phones presently in use are paid for by companies, rather than individuals.

CELLULAR MOBILITY

Cellular phones are not limited to cars. Several models are small enough to be carried in a purse or briefcase. Some predict that eventually everyone will carry a personal portable phone rather than rely on phones attached to the walls in their houses. Another innovation will be computerized cellular phones that will display the number of the caller or divert certain calls to a message center, allowing the receiver to screen the calls.

As the use of cellular phones increases, the current cells will be subdivided into smaller cells. Similarly, as cellular phone usage increases, prices are expected to decrease. The price of a cellular phone currently depends on the number of features. Some have voice recognition for hands-free dialing. Some can tell you how long your call was, time your current call, and add up the total number of calls you have made. However, cellular phone use is not expected to become popular with the mass consumer market until the end of the century.

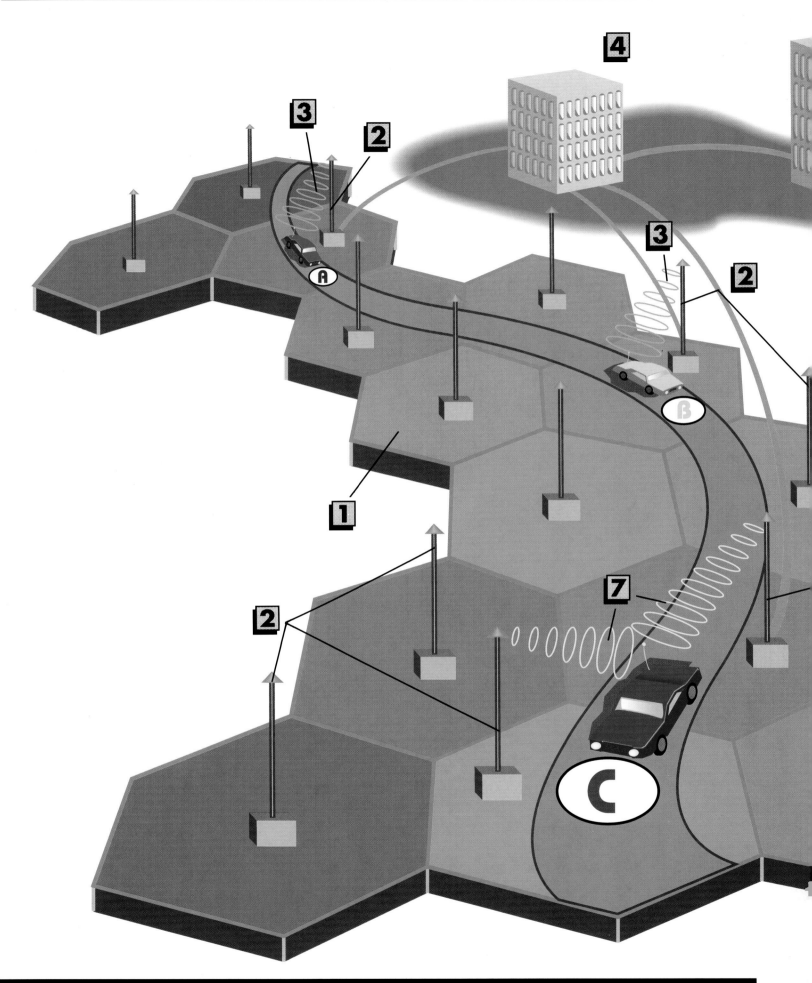

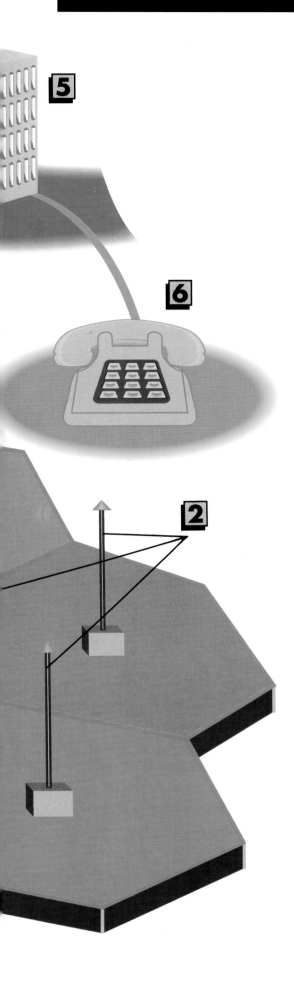

In this diagram, which shows the network of geographically divided cells, a call made from a stationary telephone to car A is routed through the central telephone office to a Mobile Telephone Switching Office to a transmitter in the cell in which car A is located. Car A may also phone car B, in which case the signal is routed from the transmitter to the MTSO to the transmitter in the cell in which car B is located. A call hand-off is illustrated as car C crosses from one cell into another and the cellular signal is transferred by the MTSO from the transmitter in the first cell to the transmitter in the second.

CELLULAR TELEPHONE

1	cell
2	transmitter
3	radio waves
4	MTSO
5	main telephone office
6	ground-based telephone
7	call hand-off

This view of a communications satellite orbiting the earth shows how microwave transmissions are beamed in a straight line to receiving stations on the planet. The cutaway area reveals many of the satellite's operating components, including control thrusters, propellant tanks, and kick motor, all of which help to control satellite in its orbit. The battery pack is necessary for power during those times when sunlight cannot reach the solar cells.

COMMUNICATIONS SATELLITE

A satellite is simply a celestial object in orbit around a larger object. Thus, the Earth is a satellite of the sun; moons are satellites of the planets they orbit. Similarly, objects that we send into space to orbit the Earth are also satellites.

There are two main kinds of nonmilitary satellites in space: communications satellites and weather satellites. Communications satellites allow the exchange of live television programs and telephone calls all over the Earth. They also keep ships in contact with their shore-based offices and with other ships. Because of communications satellites, millions of people are able to enjoy events, such as the Olympics, as they happen, rather than having to watch highlights on the nightly news after the fact.

Communications satellites operate by receiving microwave signals from an Earth station, amplifying (increasing) them, and then transmitting them back to Earth. Any station in the region to which the signals are beamed can pick them up. There are Earth stations in more than 100 countries.

MICROWAVE TRANSMISSIONS

Microwaves are extremely high-frequency radio waves. They are transmitted by parabolic (bowl-shaped) antennas, commonly referred to as satellite dishes. The dish reflects outgoing waves from the transmit horn in a narrow beam toward the earth, and directs incoming signals to the receiving horn. The advantage of satellite communications over land-based communications is that there is no need to lay thousands of miles or kilometers of cable, or, as in the case of a ground-based microwave system, to build relay stations. Since the waves move forward in narrow, straight lines (they don't bend with the curvature of the earth), land-based microwave repeater stations must be placed very near one another. As a result, transoceanic microwave transmissions were not possible until satellites were developed. From space, the waves can beam straight down to points on Earth.

Communications satellites are powered by solar energy (see page 112), which is collected by solar cells that cover the sides of the satellite. During the times of the year when the satellite is not exposed to sunlight, batteries power the equipment until the satellite's orbit brings it back into view of the sun.

COMMUNICATIONS SATELLITE

1   control thruster
2   thermal radiator
3   antenna feeds
4   telemetry and command antenna
5   antenna reflector
6   traveling wave tube amplifier
7   battery pack
8   solar cell arrays
9   apogee kick motor
10   propellant tank

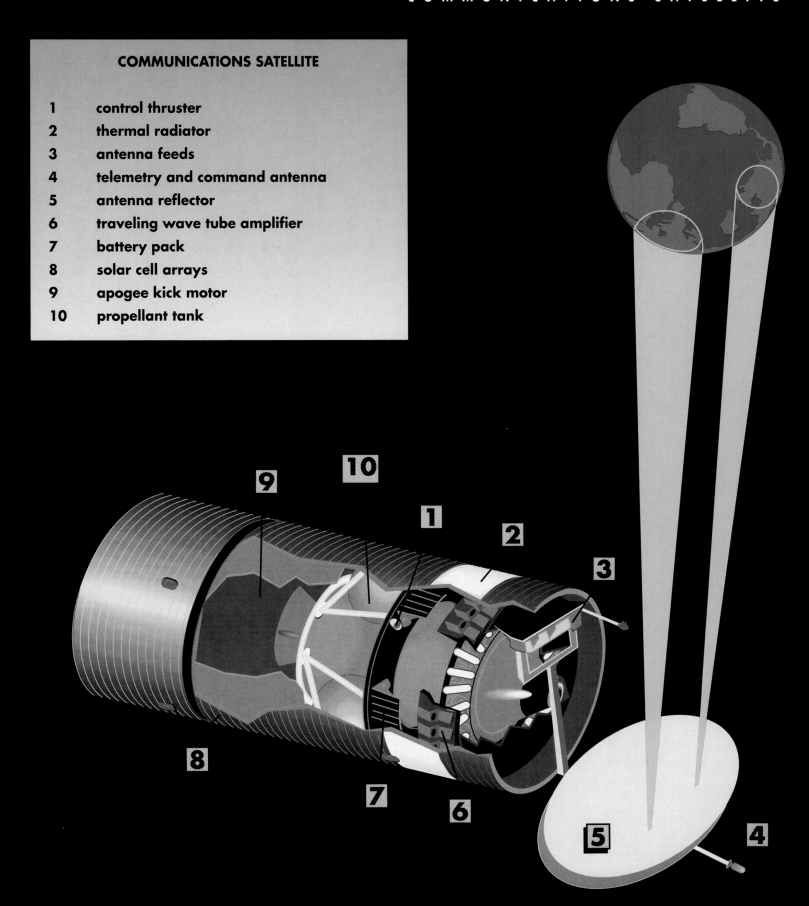

SATELLITE DEVELOPMENT

Satellites are launched into space atop rockets. The first satellite launched, of course, was the Soviet *Sputnik*, in October of 1957, followed by the United States' first satellite launch on December 18, 1958. This satellite, an experiment of the United States government's project SCORE (Signal Communication by Orbiting Relay Equipment), recorded messages on magnetic tape and retransmitted them. This satellite was short-lived—it functioned for thirteen days, after which its batteries ran out of power. It was destroyed when it entered Earth's atmosphere on January 21, 1959.

American Telephone and Telegraph (AT&T) launched *Telstar* on July 10, 1962. This satellite had a microwave receiver and transmitter, and it was the first to transmit live television and telephone conversations across the Atlantic, although it did so on an experimental basis. Because *Telstar* orbited the earth, it moved out of range of its transmitting and receiving stations most of the time, and could be used for only a few hours each day.

Syncom 2 and *Syncom 3*, launched in 1963 and 1964 respectively, were the first satellites with synchronous orbits—that is, they moved at the same speed as the rotation of the earth. *Syncom 3* transmitted the opening ceremonies of the Olympic Games in Tokyo. Today, satellites are often situated above a particular point on the earth, where they remain, in geostationary orbits. As satellite technology advanced, it became clear that international satellite communication required the cooperation of many countries, so the International Telecommunications Satellite Organization (Intelsat) was established. Intelsat began as a joint venture in August 1964, when eleven countries agreed to form a global communications system. Currently, about 100 countries are involved. Intelsat is responsible for all international non-military satellite communication outside the Soviet Union.

A recent development in satellite communications is very small aperture terminals (VSAT). These higher-powered satellites can transmit information to small Earth stations. VSATs are used by such businesses as auto dealerships, banks (for automated tellers), brokerage firms, hotel and airline reservation systems, and retail stores.

In this artist's conception, (opposite page and above) a g-star communications satellite is in a geostationary orbit—that is, positioned above a particular point on the equator. As it orbits the Earth, it may receive telephone calls, television signals, or other information from a ground station in North America, which it can then beam to a ground station in Europe.

WEATHER SATELLITES

Weather satellites collect information about weather patterns occurring all over the Earth and transmit it to earth receiving stations in the same way as communications satellites. Several Geostationary Operational Environment Satellites, or GOES, each monitor a different portion of the Earth. These satellites are operated by the United States National Oceanic and Atmospheric Administration (NOAA), and are part of the World Weather Watch project, which includes Japan's GMS and Europe's Meteosat weather satellites.

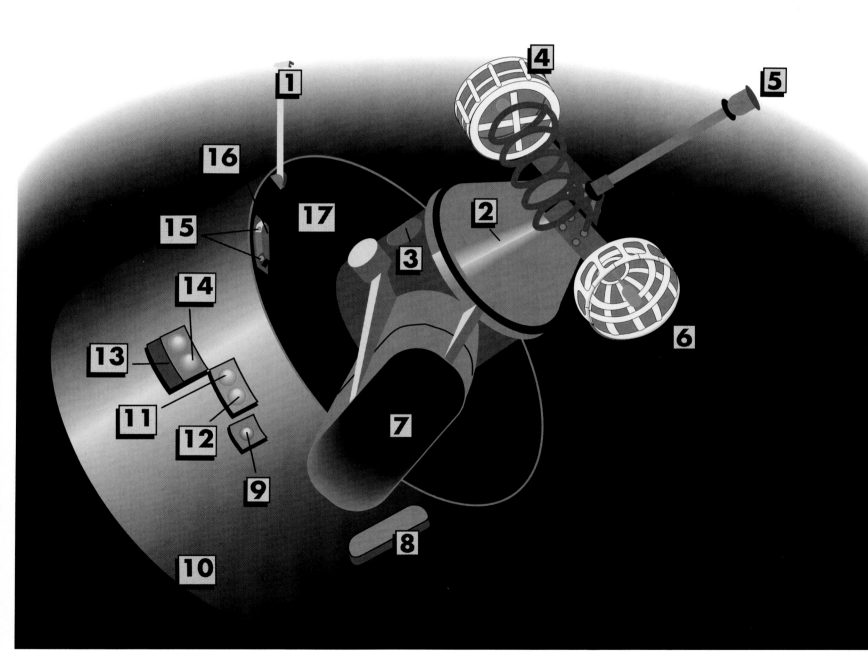

GOES sense the radiant energy produced by the earth and clouds using an instrument called a visible and infrared spin scan radiometer atmospheric sounder (VAS). The VAS detects temperature variations throughout the atmosphere and combines that information with the sensed radiant energy to provide a weather profile at various altitudes. Visual and infrared images are transmitted to Earth, and the data is used for storm evaluation and providing information on cloud cover, winds, ocean currents, fog distribution, and other weather activity.

GOES sends pictures back to Earth every thirty minutes. NOAA's receiving station at Wallops Island, Virginia, processes the images and sends them out all over the country. These are the satellite pictures seen on television weather reports and in the newspaper.

The frequent transmissions allow meteorologists to trace storms and provide ample warnings for events such as floods and hurricanes. For example, one GOES monitored the eruption of Mount St. Helens in Washington State and tracked its plume of volcanic ash as it spread across the United States.

METEOROLOGICAL INFORMATION GATHERING

GOES also has a data collection system that receives information on a regular basis from instruments on the ground, such as rain and river gauges, seismometers, buoys, and automatic weather stations. These instruments can contact the satellite in the event of an unusual weather change.

GOES-F, the third GOES satellite, is 7 feet (2 m) wide, 11.5 feet (4 m) tall, and weighs 880 lbs (400 kg). On board is a space environment monitor, which detects solar protons and electrons, alpha particles, X rays, and magnetic fields in space. This information is used for high-altitude commercial flights, space shuttle missions, telecommunications, and monitoring the distribution of electricity.

In addition to tracking flood and hurricane activity, weather satellites help scientists observe changes in the oceans, watch for volcanic activity on Earth, study the effects of drought, find mineral deposits, measure the destruction of the rain forests, study nuclear test sites, and pinpoint earthquake faults.

Landsat is a weather satellite that transmits information for making maps on seismic activity, wildlife, climates, landslides, avalanches, and pollution. *Landsat V*, the newest Landsat, has a device that is highly sensitive to the bands of the electromagnetic spectrum. This device picks up electromagnetic radiation from the earth, turns it into codes, and sends the codes to Earth-based receiving stations.

With a variety of such specially designed satellites collecting specific data, we can put together a very detailed picture of the earth.

The GOES satellite's instruments gather different types of information: the VAS detects radiant energy and temperature changes on Earth, assisting meteorologists in predicting weather changes. The X-ray sensor measures X-rays from the sun, which helps to detect solar flares. The magnetometer monitors the magnetic field in geostationary orbit, while the Energetic Particle Sensor (EPS) telescope measures energetic particle flux in orbit. The antennas both transmit and receive mission, telemetry, and command data.

	WEATHER SATELLITE
1	magnetometer
2	despun section
3	VAS
4	UHF antenna
5	S-band bicone omni antenna
6	S-band high gain
7	VAS sunshade
8	x-ray sensor
9	hepad
10	solar panels
11	EPS telescope
12	EPS dome
13	sun sensors
14	earth sensors
15	radial thrusters
16	axial thruster
17	thermal barrier

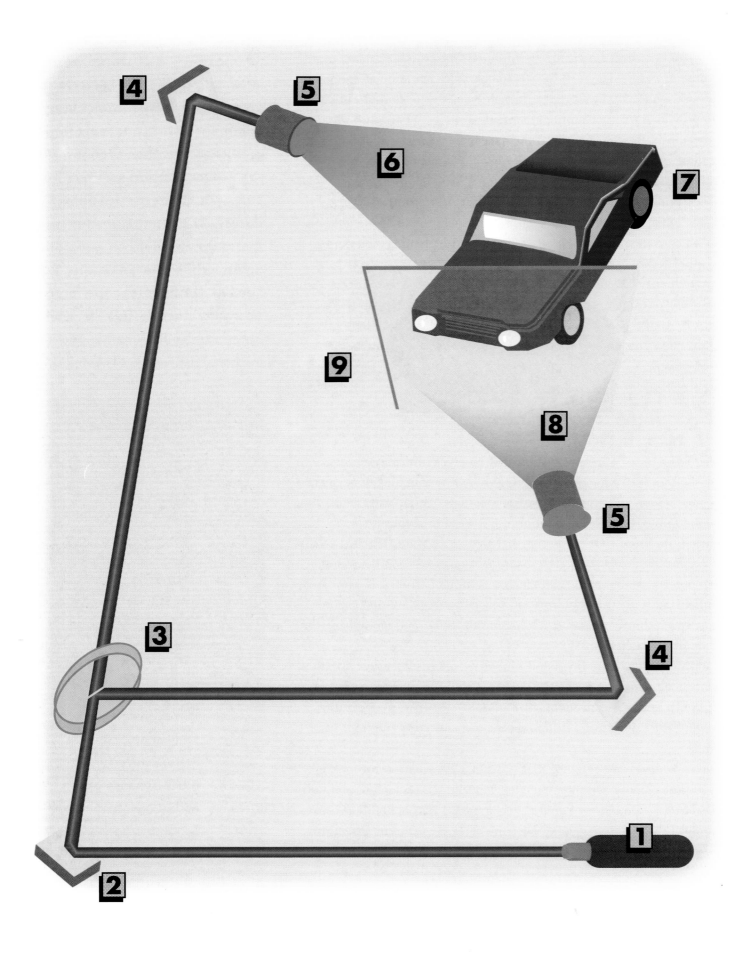

HOLOGRAM

Holography is a method of creating three-dimensional images—or projected images—using laser technology (see also laser surgery, page 92). While ordinary photography simply records the variations in light intensity reflected from an object, holography also records the way in which the light waves relate to one another. Hungarian scientist Dennis Gabor invented holography in 1948, for which he received the Nobel prize in physics in 1971.

LASER TECHNOLOGY

A hologram is not actually a picture of a scene or object, but rather a collection of information about the scene, coded in the form of light rays known as interference patterns. To produce a hologram, all the light rays must be of the same wavelength—such light rays are only possible using a laser. Holograms are made using photographic plates or film that receive laser light from two separate sources. The object beam is light reflected directly from the object of the hologram. The reference beam lights the photographic plate or film. In a reflection hologram (as opposed to a transmission hologram, which must be viewed with a laser) the beams strike opposite sides of the plate or film.

The object beam and the reference beam meet in the photographic plate or film. As they meet, the individual pairs of light rays in the beams (one ray from every point on the object and a mate from the reference beam) interfere with one another, creating an "interference pattern." Interference may be "constructive," producing light, or "destructive," producing dark—the pattern will vary according to the surface brightness of the object.

When the plate or film is developed, the interference pattern is contained in layers of silver (from the photographic emulsion). Light hitting the hologram penetrates the layers and is reflected by them, so that the light waves diverge. When you look at a hologram, your eyes see many points formed by the sets of layers of the interference pattern—indeed, each eye sees a different part of the hologram in the reflected light waves. The brain puts the images together to form a single, three-dimensional picture. When you change the angle of viewing, a different set of light rays is reflected, and you see another view of the image.

In making a hologram of an object, laser light is directed towards a mirror, which reflects it into a beam splitter. The beam splitter is a semi-silvered mirror that actually splits the laser beam, sending part of it on and reflecting the rest. The first, or object, beam goes to another mirror, which reflects it into a beam spreading lens, through which it illuminates the object of the hologram. The second, or reference, beam is reflected to a mirror and into another beam spreader, through which it illuminates a film plate. The film receives light from both the object itself and the reference beam. When the light rays from each source meet, they "inter-fere," creating a pattern in the film.

MAKING A HOLOGRAM

1 laser
2 mirror
3 beam splitter
4 mirror
5 beam-spreading lens
6 object beam
7 object
8 reference beam
9 photographic plate

This hologram by holographer Nicholas Phillips, titled "Digital," shows a circuit board with a section seen through a magnifying glass. As the viewer changes position, the view seen through the magnifying glass also shifts.

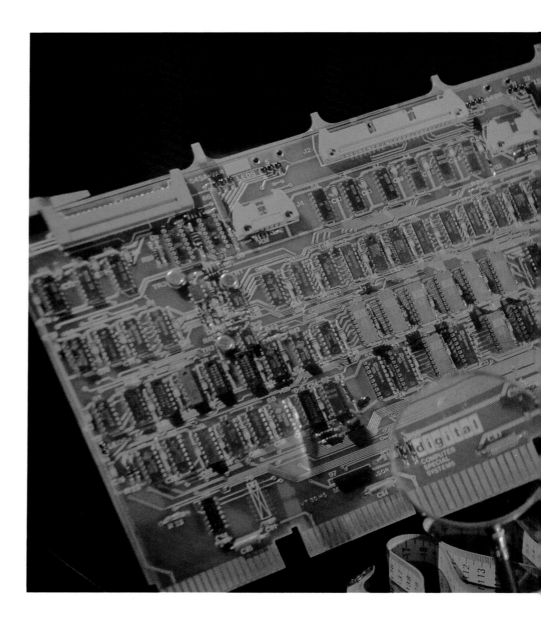

APPLICATIONS

Holography can be used to photograph difficult and inaccessible regions of an object. Perhaps a deep depression in an object cannot be studied via microscope, for instance, because the distance is too long. Light can reach it, however, and so the resulting holographic image can be studied under the microscope, since it is three dimensional. Other uses include recognizing patterns, detecting minute motions of objects, viewing inside structures, and getting magnification so great that even some of the structure of atoms can be seen. This technique is called holographic interferometry, or holometry, and can be used in laser surgery.

Holograms can also be made with sound waves, via computers, and with microwaves. Holographic "movies" can be made, as well, which give viewers a different perspective, depending on where they look from. Someday, we may even have holographic TV.

Interference is the key to holography. The interference pattern is contained in layers of silver when the hologram is developed. When light strikes the hologram, it penetrates the layers of the interference pattern and is reflected back. The eyes each see different images from the points of light reflected from the hologram. The brain forms the images into a single, 3-dimensional representation of the object.

SEEING A HOLOGRAM

1 left eye vision
2 right eye vision
3 light rays
4 layers of silvered paper
5 3-dimensional image of object

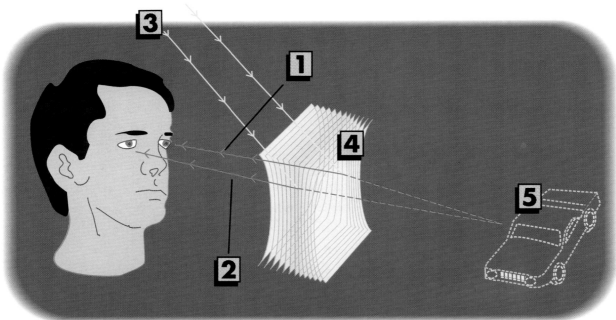

PART THREE
MEDICAL TECHNOLOGY

ULTRASOUND

Over the past forty years, ultrasound (formerly called sonography), has become one of the most widely used and accepted procedures for diagnosing medical problems. Requiring no surgery, ultrasound is a non-invasive, safe, painless, and inexpensive way of producing images of the body's "soft" tissues.

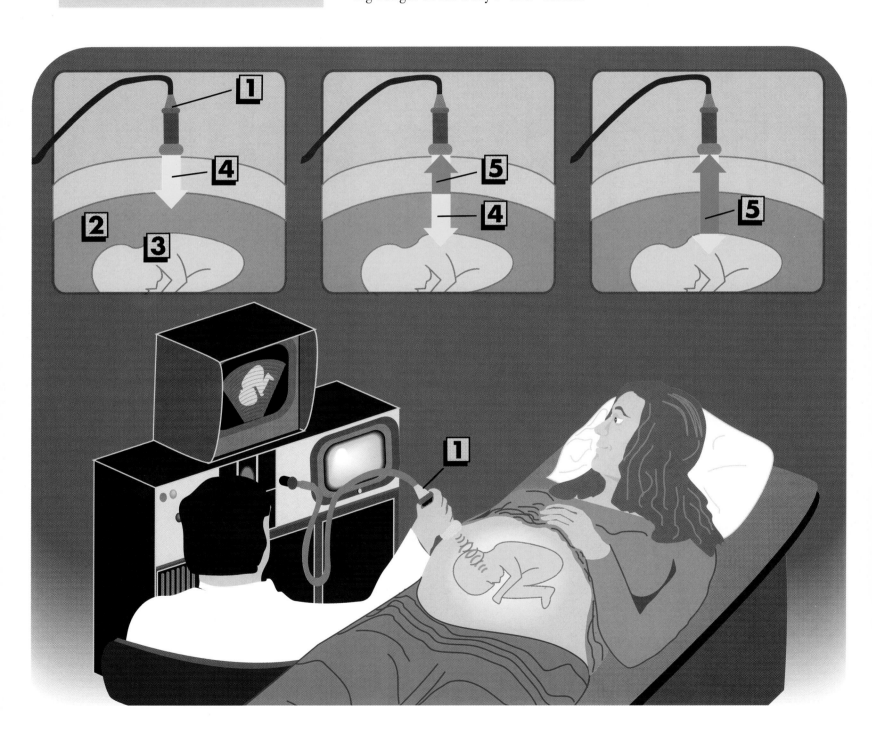

Other methods are available for viewing the body, such as X rays. X rays, however, cannot view soft tissue, and there is a risk of radiation damage. Ultrasound uses high-frequency sound waves, which pose no risk to the body's tissues. Ultrasound can distinguish one type of tissue from another and can also show internal motion, making it an excellent diagnostic tool.

Several types of doctors use ultrasound to examine their patients. Radiologists use it to identify sites of tumors and other masses. Cardiologists use it to study heart motion, not only the chambers, vessel, walls, and valves, but also the blood flow. Vascular surgeons use ultrasound to detect and locate obstructions in blood vessels. Obstetrician/gynecologists (ob/gyns) use it to check fetal development. Sometimes the baby is in a position where the ultrasound can reveal whether it is a boy or a girl. Ultrasound can also be used to study the uterus and ovaries to evaluate pelvic masses and to determine sources of infertility in women.

USING SOUND WAVES TO LOOK INTO THE BODY

An ultrasound examination is a fairly simple process. A transducer, a device that produces and receives high-frequency sound waves and converts them into electrical signals, is placed against the body and slowly passed over the area to be examined.

Sound waves are emitted from the transducer and pass into the body. These sound pulses hit the body's structures and send echoes back to the transducer. Different types of tissue produce different echoes, which are separated by the transducer, and translated into electrical signals.

As the echoes are fed back into the transducer, a picture of the scanned area begins to form on a monitor. The image represents a cross section of the area.

Ultrasound cannot be used to view air spaces in the body (lungs, for example) because the sound waves need a solid or liquid medium to create an echo. There are therapeutic uses for ultrasound, however, using higher sound intensities. These include removal of dental plaque, cataract surgery, and tumor destruction.

Color-flow imaging is the newest type of ultrasound technology. Normal ultrasound displays only in black, white, and gray. Color-flow imaging places color in areas where blood is present, allowing ultrasound to be used to check an unborn baby's blood flow, look for heart defects, or see if the umbilical cord is wrapped around the baby's neck. New uses and techniques for ultrasound continue to be developed.

Opposite page: The transducer sends and receives silent, high-frequency sound waves, which pass through the mother's skin into her body and that of the fetus. As the waves strike various different types of tissue, organs, fluid, blood, and bones, they send back different echoes, which are picked up by the transducer. Below: The data from the transducer is translated into electrical signals that are fed into a computer. The signals, which vary depending on the depth of the echo, are translated into points of light on a video monitor. The points form an image on the screen.

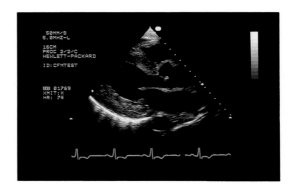

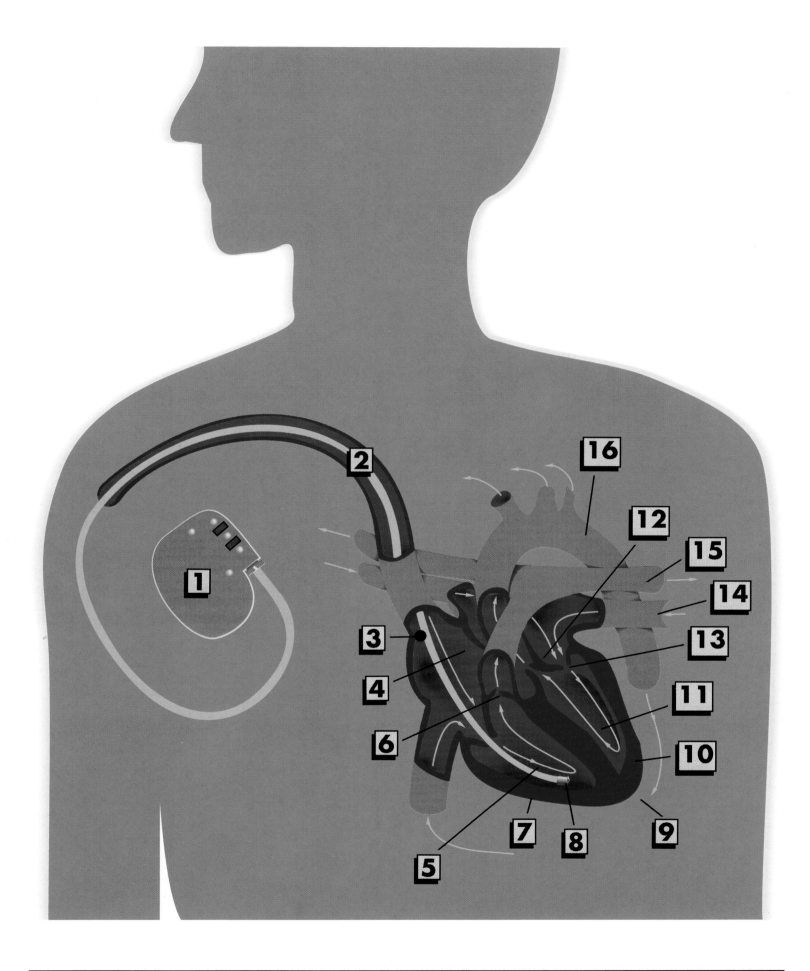

PACEMAKER

The pacemaker is an electronic device implanted in a person's chest to regulate the heartbeat. Pacemaker technology (the size and metals used) evolved as a direct spin-off of the space program.

There are two types of pacemakers: external and internal. The external type has been around since the 1930s. The pacemaker itself is implanted inside the chest, but the power supply is external. Wires protrude from the pacemaker to a battery pack carried on the arm. In contrast, with the internal type, both the pacemaker and its tiny power pack are completely implanted inside the chest.

The heart is the human body's strongest muscle. It contracts and expands to pump blood through the system. Before it can contract, however, it must receive an electric signal. That signal normally comes from the heart's natural pacemaker, a part of the heart called the sinus node, which is located in the muscle of the upper right atrium chamber. It generates signals at regular intervals, ensuring that the heart supplies blood to the body at the required rate, depending on the body's needs. During exercise, for example, the heart rate speeds up to pump more blood and deliver more oxygen to the body; during sleep, it slows down. Heart disease causes some people to be unable to maintain a normal heart rhythm. The natural impulses may become irregular—too fast, too slow, or too weak—or the signals may be blocked. This disruption of the regular impulses is known as impaired conduction. A person suffering from this condition may feel weak, dizzy, or tired. This arrhythmia can lead to other problems, even cardiac arrest. Before pacemakers, people suffering from such a condition might have died. With pacemakers, however, they can lead normal, active lives.

Two inventors are credited with inventing the pacemaker. In 1952, Dr. Paul Zoll invented an external pacemaker that delivered electrical shocks to the heart. For this and other work, he became known as "the father of the pacemaker." In 1957, Dr. C. Walton Lillihei and TV repairman Earl Bakken joined forces, and Bakken built a pacemaker to Lillihei's specifications in just one month. Earl Bakken started a company, called Medtronics, to make pacemakers. Today Medtronics is the world's largest supplier of pacemakers.

External pacemakers were the earliest form, and they are still used during open-heart surgery and after bypass operations to regulate the heartbeat. External pacemakers carry a lower risk of infection or hemorrhage because opening the chest isn't necessary. They can also be used when an internal pacemaker is being changed or when the patient is under deep anesthesia and an irregular heartbeat can develop.

This pacemaker has been implanted just below the skin of the chest. The pacing lead wire is inserted into the heart. Like the heart's natural pacemaker, the sinus node, the artificial pacemaker sends electrical impulses to the inner wall of the heart, causing it to contract, or pump, at regular intervals appropriate to the body's activity level.

	PACEMAKER
1	power pack/pulse generator
2	pacing lead
3	sinus node
4	right atrium
5	right ventricle
6	valve
7	myocardium (heart muscle)
8	electrode
9	pericardium (surrounding tissue)
10	endocardium (inside lining)
11	left ventricle
12	left atrium
13	valve
14	pulmonary vein
15	pulmonary artery
16	aorta

PACEMAKER FACT AND FICTION

FICTION

Microwave ovens can harm pacemakers. Pacemaker wearers should not go near them.

Metal detectors at airports will damage pacemakers. Wearers should avoid them.

Large electrical motors can confuse the electronic circuitry in a pacemaker.

FACT

Microwaves have no effect on modern pacemakers—the radiated microwave field outside the oven is harmless.

The metal detector may beep to indicate the presence of a pacemaker, but it will not harm or affect the pacemaker at all.

Pacemakers are rarely affected by everyday electrical appliances, tools, or motors. If a pacemaker wearer suspects interference from any such device, he or she should simply turn it off or move away from it. A physician can advise a patient regarding any special circumstances. Electrosurgery and magnetic resonance imaging may affect a pacemaker, but these procedures are performed under medical supervision, minimizing any risk.

This chest x-ray shows a pacemaker in place. A wire leads from the power pack to the heart, where an electrode at the wire's tip stimulates the heart muscle.

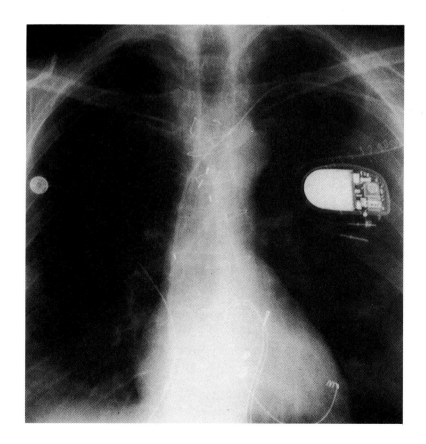

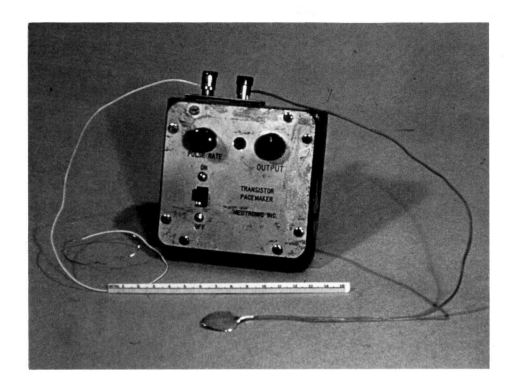

This is the original Medtronics pacemaker, designed by Earl Bakken and Dr. Lillihei in 1957.

MONITORING AND REGULATING HEARTBEAT

Today's pacemakers are small, sensitive instruments that can monitor the heart's performance and deliver appropriate stimulation when necessary, restoring regularity to the pulse. The pacemaker has three basic parts: the pulse generator (containing the power source and circuitry), leads to the heart (flexible, insulated wires), and the programmer (a small computer used by the physician to set the pacemaker's parameters).

The pulse generator houses the battery, which has a life span of five to fifteen years, and the circuitry. A tiny computer, the circuitry is capable of receiving information from the heart and transforming energy from the battery into electrical signals to stimulate the heart as needed. Thus, when the heart is beating normally, the pacemaker simply monitors the situation until action is needed.

When the microcircuits send an electrical signal to the heart, it is carried by the lead wires. One end of the lead is attached to the pulse generator by the connector; the other end is a platinum electrode connected to the heart. Through this electrode, impulses stimulate the heart tissue, causing the heart to beat; the electrode also senses the heart's natural activity, and sends the information back through the lead to the circuitry.

The pacemaker can be implanted in a simple procedure that takes less than an hour, and is performed using local anesthesia. The surgeon slips the lead into a vein and guides it to the heart. The pulse generator fits into a pocket of the shoulder or abdomen. When the battery wears out, a new pulse generator is implanted to replace the old.

LASER SURGERY

The word *laser* stands for Light Amplification by Stimulated Emission of Radiation. Although Albert Einstein thought of the principles of laser light in 1916, a laser was not actually built until 1960, when Theodore Maiman pioneered this technology.

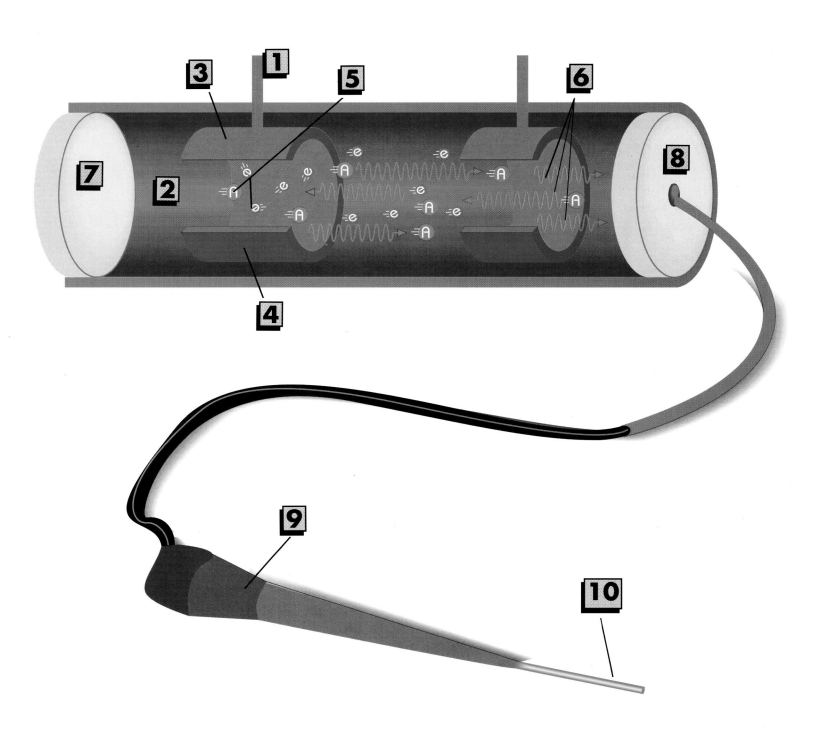

Laser beams are narrow, intense rays of either bright, visible light or invisible infrared rays. The light may be a continuous beam or a series of brief pulses. To create a laser, energy must be produced in a "lasing medium," which may be solid, liquid, or gas. The energy is pumped into a tube of the lasing medium, exciting atoms, which then produce photons, or light particles, when stimulated. Mirrors at the ends of the tube reflect the light rays, causing more photons to be released. When the light becomes very intense, a small portion passes through one of the mirrors, creating a narrow beam of intense light.

Every laser beam has four characteristics that make it different from the light from a light bulb. Laser light has a very narrow focus—it is not spread out over distances. This quality is called "directionality." The light waves from a specific laser share the same wavelength and vibrate at the same speed. This quality is called "coherence," and accounts for the intensity of laser light—its ability to send a lot of power to a small area. Laser light is also "monochromatic," meaning that it has only one color.

Three types of lasers are used in medicine today: the argon laser and the carbon dioxide laser, both gas-based, and the YAG (yttrium aluminum garnet) laser, which is crystal-based. The argon laser is low-powered and sends out a high electrical charge. Some uses for this laser are to fix ulcers, destroy certain tumors of the bladder, remove birthmarks, and treat glaucoma. The carbon dioxide laser is a high-powered, high-precision surgical "knife," which cuts only to a depth of 0.1 mm on each pass. This is particularly valuable in brain and spinal surgery. The YAG is the newest laser and can cut very deeply into tissue. It is also used in eye surgery, and can vaporize large tumors, but cannot be used in precision surgery.

Laser light is extremely useful in surgery for a number of reasons. It is sterile, due to the heat it produces, so risk of infection is greatly reduced. It is extremely precise, allowing delicate procedures to be performed safely. Furthermore, lasers can penetrate otherwise inaccessible areas of the body, permitting organs to be repaired without being removed. In addition, lasers can destroy abnormal tissue while leaving healthy tissue alone. They speed healing, minimize complications, and can reduce convalescent time significantly.

When energy from an external power source is pumped into the laser cavity, the lasing medium produces photons (light particles emitted by excited atoms). The photons are reflected by mirrors within the cavity, causing the rays of light to strike other atoms, exciting them to produce more photons. Light energy increases within the cavity until it becomes bright enough to pass through the semi-silvered mirror as a laser beam.

LASER SURGERY

1	power source
2	lasing medium
3	laser cavity
4	electrode
5	excited atoms produce photons
6	light rays vibrate at same frequency
7	mirror
8	semi-silvered mirror
9	surgical device
10	laser beam

MAGNETIC RESONANCE IMAGING

When scanning a section of the body, the computer establishes a grid of tiny boxes, or voxels, in 3 dimensions. The magnetic field is varied in one direction, head to toe, to define the area of interest. Within this section, the protons (normally random) will wobble at a single given frequency. Radio frequency coils then emit a pulse to topple the protons. Before they can re-align themselves, other coils change the magnetic strength of the plane in another direction, top to bottom, causing the protons to wobble at different rates. Once again, coils vary the magnetic field, this time left to right, causing the protons to wobble at different frequencies again. In this way, the computer locates all the voxels in each direction.

MRI stands for "magnetic resonance imaging." It produces detailed images of the human body using a magnetic field and radio waves. Originally called Nuclear Magnetic Resonance (NMR), it was discovered by Dr. Raymond Davadian, who developed the first machine in the 1970s. One of the most exciting advances in radiology, MRI can determine the chemical makeup of cells in the body without using radiation.

MAGNETIC RESONANCE IMAGING

1	magnetic coil
2	random protons
3	protons aligned
4	protons varied
5	radio waves
6	computer
7	image on screen

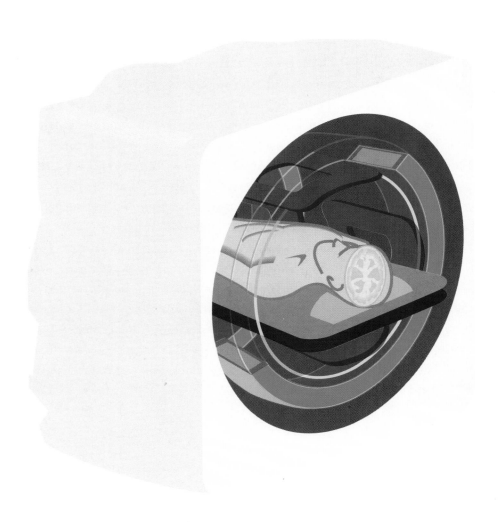

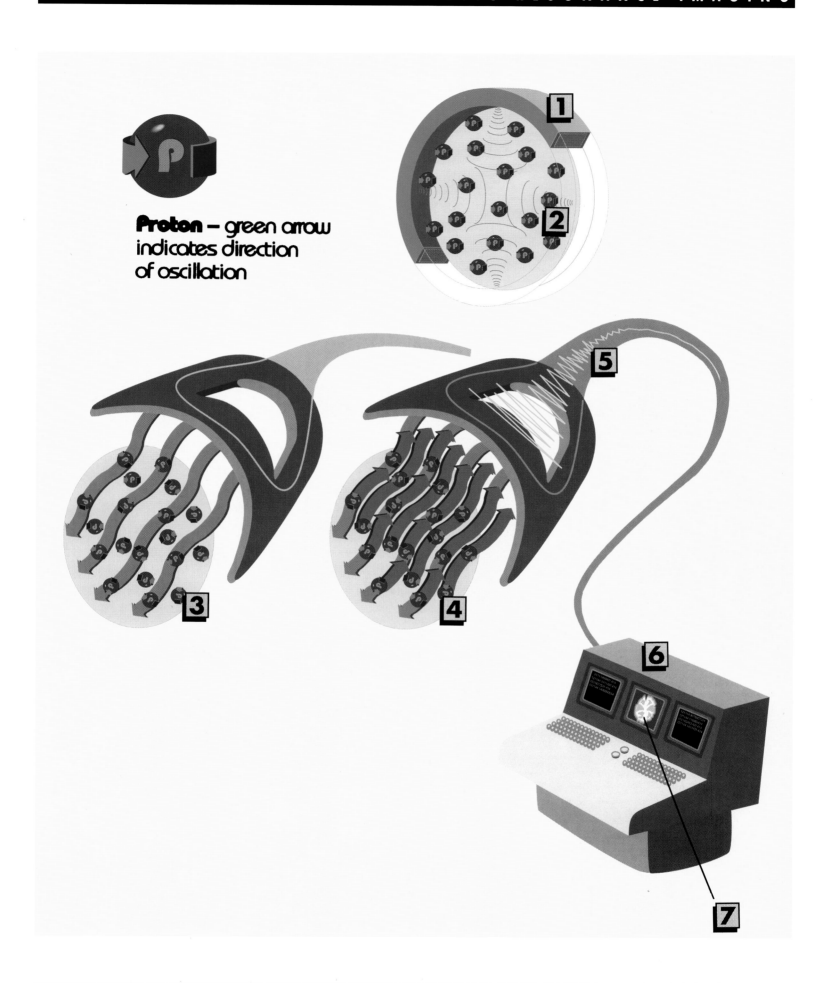

Proton – green arrow indicates direction of oscillation

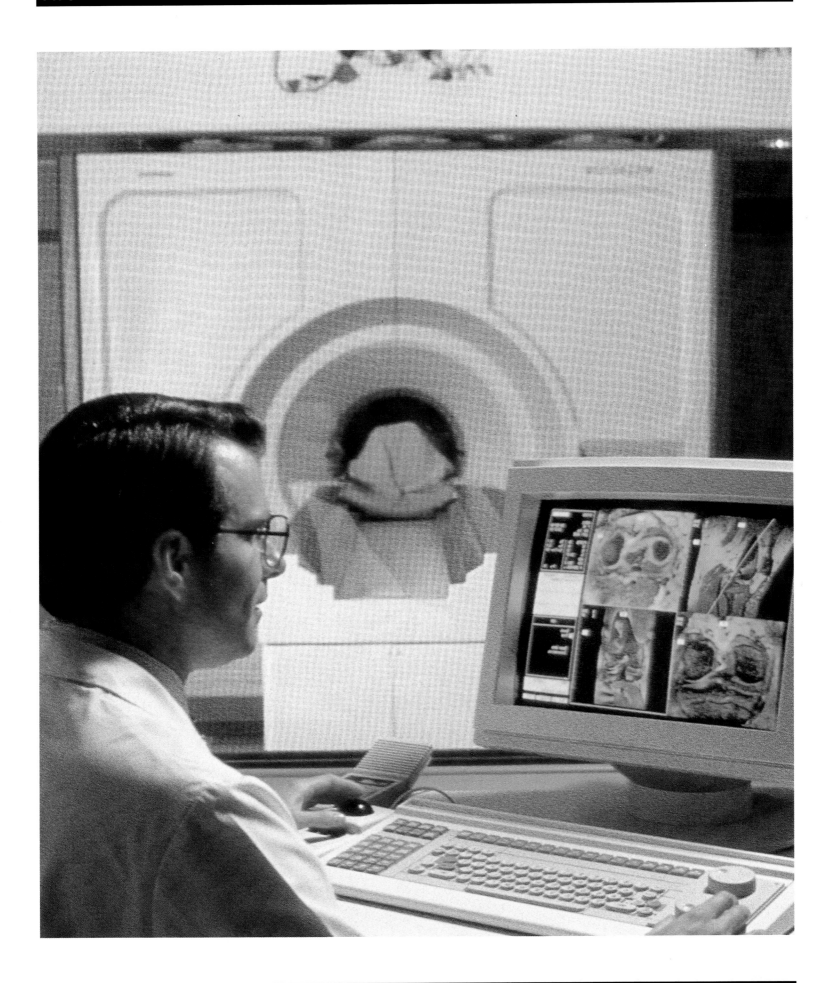

MAGNETIC IMAGES

The magnetic resonance imager is basically a giant magnet. The scanner is a tube, shaped almost like a large doughnut. The patient lies on a non-magnetic table that slides into the scanner. Inside the scanner are ring-shaped electromagnets, which produce a magnetic field.

Each of the atoms in the body has a proton. Normally, the protons spin randomly. When the patient lies inside the MRI, the scanner creates a strong magnetic field. This magnetic field makes the protons rotate in the same direction and line up in all of the body's atoms. Then a radio signal is beamed into the magnetic field, disturbing the uniform movement of the protons, which then release energy. When the signal ceases, the protons line up again. Detectors in the scanner measure the released energy and the time required for the protons to realign. The information picked up from the atoms is sent to a computer, which builds a three-dimensional image from the signals. Because it stores information about the entire body part that is scanned, the computer can show different, precise "slices" of the tissue anytime they are needed. The images on the screen are recorded on film or tape, making a permanent record. The MRI gives detailed information about the type of tissue it scans and its condition. It can therefore detect infections, malignancies, spinal and joint abnormalities, brain and nervous system disorders, heart disease, and musculoskeletal injuries. The patient feels nothing when being scanned, and the MRI is safer than X rays because it uses no harmful radiation. The room that houses the MRI is shielded to prevent any stray radio waves from interfering with the procedure.

There is one hazard, however, called the "projectile effect." Metal objects such as pens, paper clips, and even sometimes larger items will be pulled rapidly into the MRI's magnets. Since these flying objects can hurt someone, all items made of metal must be removed from the room before the MRI is used. Therefore, the MRI is not recommended for use on patients with pacemakers or those with implants, shrapnel, or other metals in their body. Tooth fillings, however, will not cause problems.

The MRI can provide extremely precise images of whatever body part it is used to scan. It allows for greater diagnostic accuracy and earlier disease detection. Although the use of magnetic fields is not known to cause any harmful effects, MRI is not recommended for pregnant women.

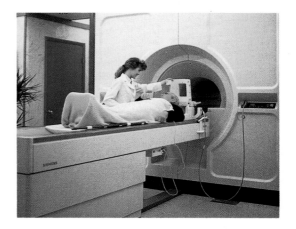

Inside the MRI unit is a magnet and radio coils, which are used to vary the frequencies at which protons in the body vibrate. This process is a non-invasive and painless way to form a 3-dimensional image of the body's tissues.

Opposite: The computer uses the number of protons in each voxel and the magnetic properties of the tissue being scanned to form a 3-dimensional image of the area on-screen. The screen image is then recorded on film or magnetic tape to produce a permanent copy.

PART FOUR

HOUSEHOLD TECHNOLOGY

MICROWAVE OVEN

Do you remember when baking potatoes took an hour and a half? Or when defrosting frozen food meant letting it sit on the kitchen counter overnight? Those were the days before microwave ovens. Microwaved baked potatoes take only eight minutes, and defrosting can be accomplished in seconds. How does the microwave oven do this?

Conventional ovens use external heat to cook food. The heat cooks the food from the outside in, meaning that the outside of the food gets hotter than the inside. That's why the outside of a roast, for example, turns brown while the inside stays red, or the outside of a cake is somewhat crusty while the inside is moist. Microwave ovens, on the other hand, do not use heat to cook. They use microwaves, which are one type of electromagnetic wave. (An electromagnetic ray or wave consists of an electric and a magnetic field vibrating at the same frequency at right angles to one another. The fields basically travel together in a pattern of waves.) Depending upon the material they encounter, microwaves can be transmitted, reflected, or absorbed. Microwave ovens use all three of these processes.

MICROWAVE COOKING

The microwave has a device inside called a magnetron. The magnetron takes power from the electrical wall outlet and uses it to create microwave beams. An antenna above the magnetron sends these microwaves to a hollow tube called a waveguide. The waveguide sends the microwaves to a stirrer, a fanlike device that reflects them all around the inside of the oven. The microwaves bounce off the metal walls and pass through any container into the food, where they are absorbed by the food's water molecules.

All living things are composed mostly of water. The water molecules in food are arranged randomly. When they are struck by a microwave, however, they rotate until they are aligned with the microwave's electromagnetic field. The microwave's field pulsates billions of times per second. As the microwaves oscillate, the water molecules align, then reverse alignment. This action shakes the molecules so that they are constantly changing position, and thereby generates heat—cooking the food. The microwaves themselves do not hold heat; only the material that absorbs them becomes hot. Because microwaves pass through glass, paper, and plastic, dishes and containers made of these materials can be safely used in a microwave oven. In addition, such objects remain cool. Not only is the container cool, but so is the inside of the microwave oven.

Metal trays, dishes, and containers reflect microwaves. Besides shielding the food from the microwaves, the metal heats up and conducts

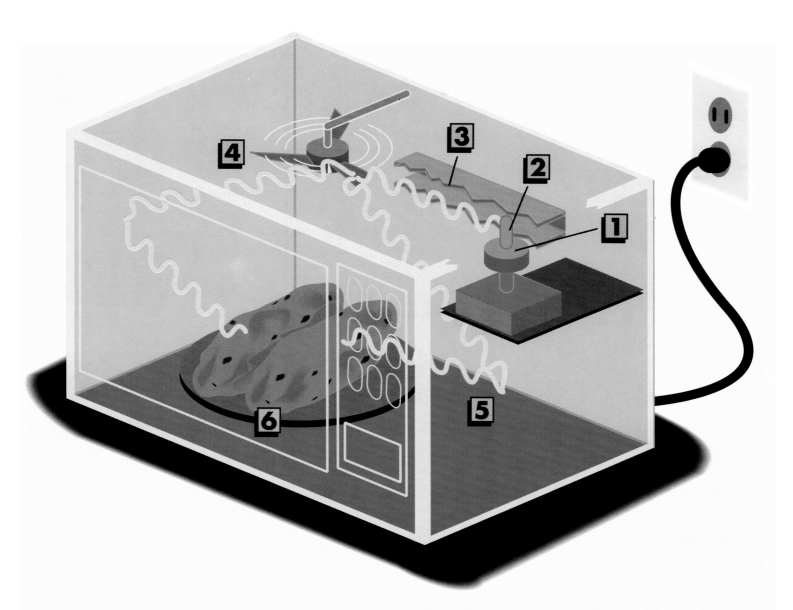

MICROWAVE OVEN

1   magnetron
2   antenna
3   waveguide
4   stirrer
5   microwaves
6   turntable

Inside a microwave oven, a magnetron produces microwaves, which are directed by an antenna to a waveguide, which passes them on to a stirrer (a spinning fan) to be dispersed in the oven, where the water molecules in the food absorb them.

electricity and could cause the oven to overload and burn out due to the amount of energy sent back to the emitter.

Aligning all the molecules in a particular type of food takes some time—but considerably less than it takes to cook food conventionally. The larger the food item, the longer it takes. The presence of salt in the water increases the heating rate.

The one type of water molecule that cannot absorb microwaves is ice. That's because the molecules in ice are locked in a crystalline structure and are therefore immobile. So how does the microwave defrost and cook frozen food? It may sound strange, but nothing is ever frozen one hundred percent. Once frozen food or ice comes into contact with air, the outer layer begins to melt. When the "frozen" item is put in the microwave, the outer melting layer absorbs the microwaves, heats up, and melts the rest of the food, which can then absorb microwaves.

One problem microwaves can encounter is steam. Steam generated from food in a closed container can cause the food to explode. That's why it is necessary to slit the plastic bags that frozen food comes in and fold back the lids of frozen food in cardboard containers.

Normal conduction ovens heat food slowly, as the warmth spreads from one part of the food to the next. Microwaves pass through the container and excite water molecules throughout the food, cooking it evenly and quickly, while leaving the container cool.

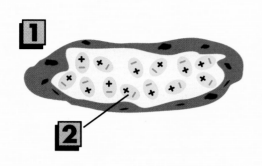

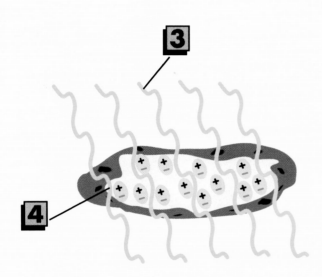

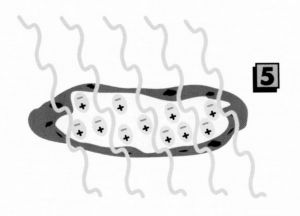

In this uncooked potato, the water molecules are randomly arranged. When the microwaves strike them, the molecules align. As the microwaves oscillate, so do the water molecules. This rapid alignment and re-alignment creates heat and cooks the food.

HOW MICROWAVES WORK

1	raw potato
2	water molecules
3	microwaves
4	molecules align
5	as molecules oscillate, potato cooks

AIR CLEANER AND IONIZER

This unit makes use of several air cleaning methods. As polluted air is drawn into the cleaner, it passes first through the prefilter, usually a mesh screen, which removes any large particles of dust or dirt. Next, the air passes through an ionizer, which charges the remaining particles positively so that they can be trapped by the negative grid in the particulate collecting plates. Finally, the air passes through a carbon filter, which absorbs any remaining odors. A fan pushes the clean air out of the unit.

Air ions, which are composed of air atoms that have taken on a positive or negative charge, were originally discovered in the 1890s by two scientists in Germany and one in England. Researchers immediately tried to prove that they were associated with biological changes in people. In fact, one scientist tried to show that too many positive ions, which occur with certain types of weather, caused people to feel ill. Since then, positive ions have been shown to be associated with migraines, nausea, irritability, and respiratory congestion.

Studies have shown that when the number of positive ions goes up, as it does on cloudy or rainy days, for instance, people become depressed or anxious or have breathing problems. The rate of murder and suicide goes up, and traffic accidents can increase by as much as 50 percent.

When negative ions fill the air, however, the opposite happens. Negative ions result from natural forces such as wind, cosmic rays, lightning, falling water (waterfalls, the shower, and surf), or radioactive gases escaping from the earth. They occur on sunny days, in open meadows, in the mountains, in pine forests, and when an emission particle from a radioactive source, such as an alpha particle, pushes an electron out of a molecule of atmospheric gas. They are in very short supply in cities, where there is so much concrete and polluted air. Even houses located in the country can have polluted air if people smoke inside or if pollen has crept in.

The scientist who finally supplied the answers to the questions about positive and negative ions was Dr. Albert Krueger, in 1960. He discovered that negative ions destroy bacteria in the air that cause colds and flu. Positive ions raise the levels of serotonin in the brain. Serotonin is a powerful hormone that helps regulate nerve impulse transmission, sleep, and mood. Serotonin acts like a "downer." Too much serotonin can cause people to become irritable and hyperactive, which can then lead to exhaustion and depression. Negative ions, on the other hand, lower the serotonin level.

The number of negative ions is especially low in office buildings because they are devoid of fresh air. Most of the windows don't open, and their air-conditioning systems, both heating and cooling, destroy ions. Cigarette smoke also destroys ions, and synthetic fibers found in carpeting, upholstery, and clothing, and also typewriters, generate positive ions. Deionized air has been shown to be very harmful to small animals. Most live only twenty-four days in a deionized environment.

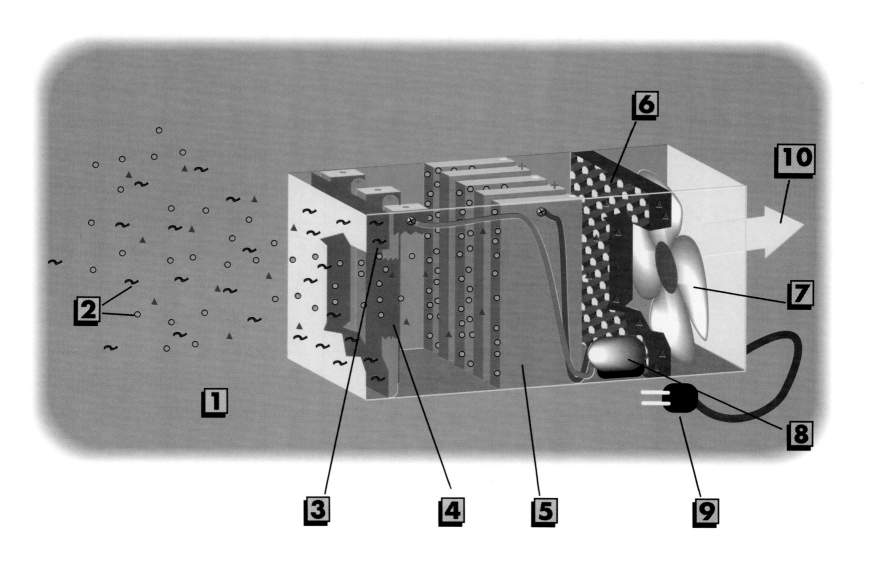

AIR CLEANER

1	polluted air
2	dust and dirt particles
3	pre-filter
4	ionizer
5	particulate collecting plates
6	carbon odor absorber
7	fan
8	power supply
9	to power source
10	clean air

A n air cleaner may include a negative ion generator in its cleaning and filtering array, resulting in the emission of clean, ion-energized air.

IONIZERS

To solve these problems, several companies have developed air ionizers—machines that pump ionized air, which is air charged with negative ions. Many people believe that breathing ionized air helps them to feel more alert and energetic and less irritable. In addition, they claim ionized air rids them of headaches, insomnia, and tension. Several studies seem to bear this out. Ionizers generate negative ions, as many as four billion per second. A group of needles in the ionizer receive a strong negative charge. An electric field is created at the end of each needle, ionizing the atoms in the air around it. Positively charged atoms are attracted to the needle, while negative ions flow away from it, into the air.

AIR CLEANING

Air cleaners often contain ionizers in addition to filters that rid the air of pollutants. Dirty air is sucked into the machine through a mesh filter that traps large particles. It then passes through an electrostatic precipitator, which sends a positive charge to any remaining particles in the air so that the second, negatively charged grid traps them. Finally, the air passes through an activated carbon filter, which removes all the odor from it. A fan then pulls the clean air out and disperses it around the room.

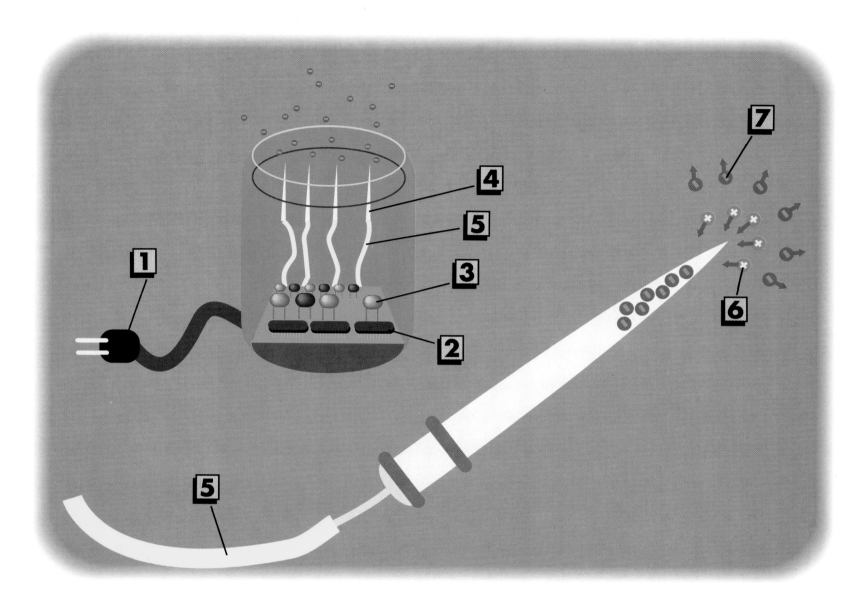

A negative ion generator works by first creating ions, then attracting the positive ions to itself so that negative ions are pushed away, into the air. A group of needle-like projections in the ionizer receive charges, causing an electrical field to form at their tips, and thereby creating ions in the air. The positive ions are attracted to the negatively charged needle, while the beneficial negative ions are repelled.

IONIZER

1	to power source
2	capacitor
3	diode
4	charged needle
5	negative charge to needle
6	positive ions
7	negative ions

CABLE TELEVISION

Not too many years ago, television viewers often had to put up with snowy pictures and poor reception. The only means of getting a stronger signal was by adjusting the antenna—either rabbit ears on top of the set itself, or an antenna on the roof. Severe storms could cause the antenna to turn, and so someone would have to climb onto the roof to adjust it. Those who lived too far from the television transmitting station or whose reception was blocked by mountains were out of luck altogether.

Cable television has changed all that. Television signals do not have to be broadcast through the air; instead they can be transmitted through wires. The wire used is called a coaxial cable. Coaxial cables can carry many different TV channels at the same time.

In a cable system, special receivers, antennas, and satellite dishes are placed in areas where they will be able to receive communications signals.

This diagram shows how the frequency band has been divided up for different uses. Specific frequencies are reserved for each use, from television transmissions to aircraft transmissions.

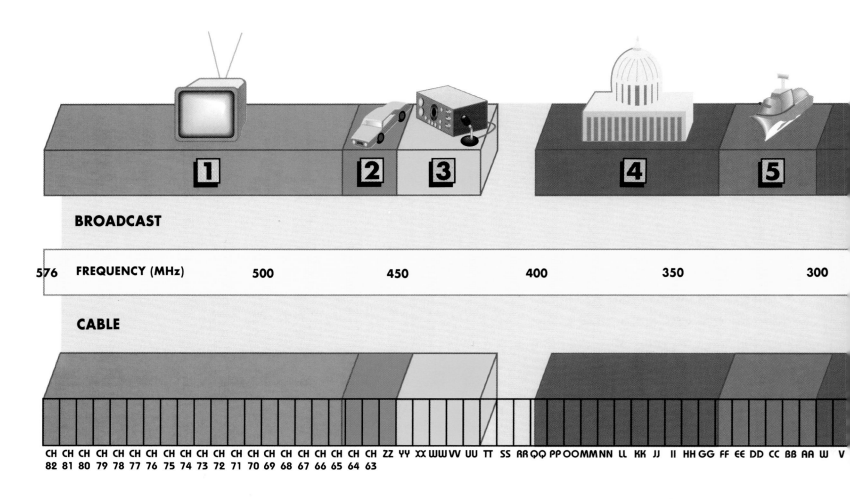

BROADCAST

| 576 | FREQUENCY (MHz) | 500 | 450 | 400 | 350 | 300 |

CABLE

CH CH CH CH CH CH CH CH CH CH CH CH CH CH CH CH CH CH CH ZZ YY XX WW VV UU TT SS RR QQ PP OO MM NN LL KK JJ II HH GG FF EE DD CC BB AA W V
82 81 80 79 78 77 76 75 74 73 72 71 70 69 68 67 66 65 64 63

These antennas pick up the signals from four main sources: over-the-air broadcasts, satellite transmissions, microwave signals, and on-site transmissions. The signals are sent to the headend, or main source, where they are amplified and sent into the cable distribution system.

The distribution system consists of three types of cables: trunk cables, feeder cables, and drop cables. The trunk cables run from the headend along the main streets. Attached to the trunk cable are the feeder cables, which branch off along the side streets. Attached to the feeder cables are the drop cables, which run into people's homes, bringing cable signals to the television. These cables can be strung in two ways: either underground, as they are in most newer areas, or on utility poles.

Cable TV is now used for educational purposes (people can take college courses on television, for instance) and to broadcast city council meetings, original programs for news, sports events, and other features not available on regular TV. Future applications include electronic mail delivery, dial-up video libraries, computer networks linked by satellite, and many other innovative services.

CABLE TELEVISION	
1	TV UHF channels
2	land mobile
3	HAM
4	government
5	marine navigation
6	TV channels 7-13
7	aircraft navigation
8	FM
9	TV channels 2-6
10	shortwave

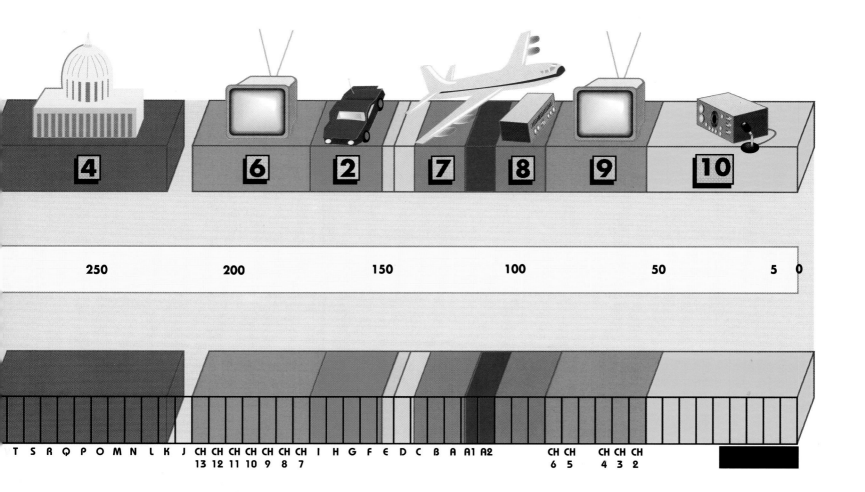

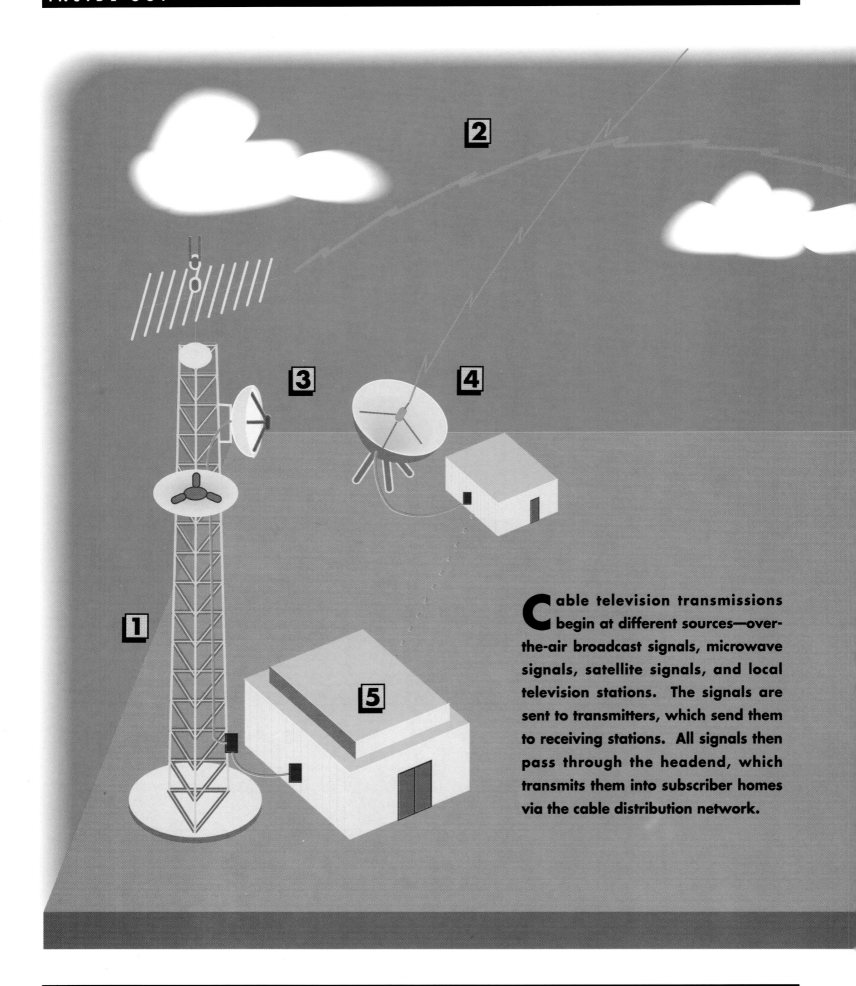

Cable television transmissions begin at different sources—over-the-air broadcast signals, microwave signals, satellite signals, and local television stations. The signals are sent to transmitters, which send them to receiving stations. All signals then pass through the headend, which transmits them into subscriber homes via the cable distribution network.

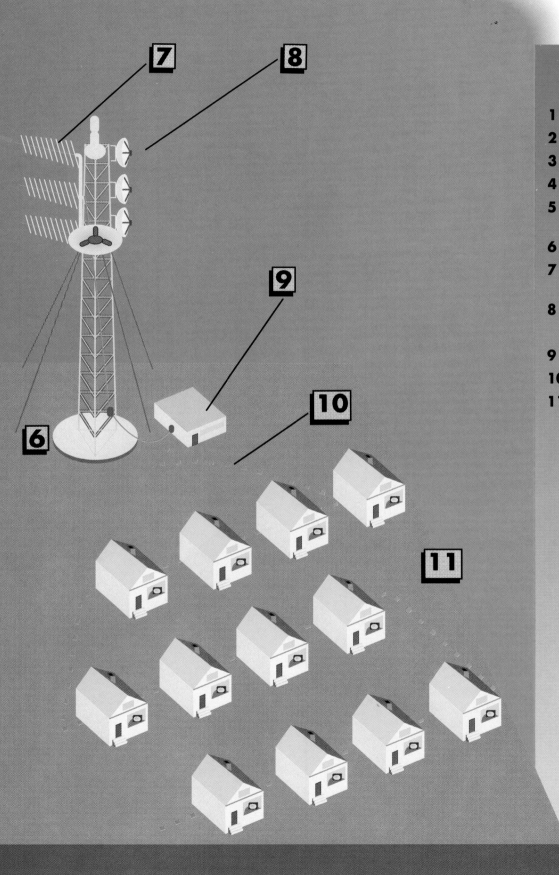

CABLE TELEVISION

1   transmitting antenna
2   over-the-air signal
3   microwave signal
4   satellite signal
5   local signal source
      (TV station)
6   receiving antenna
7   over-the-air signal
      antenna
8   microwave signal
      antenna
9   headend building
10   coaxial cable
11   cable subscriber homes

SOLAR ENERGY

The solar collector plates on this roof absorb the sun's rays, heating water that flows through copper or aluminum tubing in the collector plates down into a heat exchanger, where it heats the home's hot water supply.

The sun is a powerful source of energy because its light can be turned into electricity cleanly, efficiently, and cheaply. Today, solar energy is used to heat and cool buildings, to heat water, to power refrigerators, and to operate engines, pumps, and sewage treatment plants. It also powers many other things, such as cars, ovens, furnaces, and even satellites.

Would you be surprised to learn that the idea of using the sun's energy is not new? Indeed, the ancient Greeks promoted the concept of solar heating. In 1839, a French physicist, Antoine Becquere, demonstrated the photovoltaic effect, from *photo* meaning "light," and *voltaic*, meaning "power." Since then, there have been a number of significant developments, culminating in the use today of photovoltaic cells, devices that convert light into energy.

A photovoltaic cell is made of two types of silicon, an upper and a lower layer of each. When light strikes the cell, it frees an electron from a

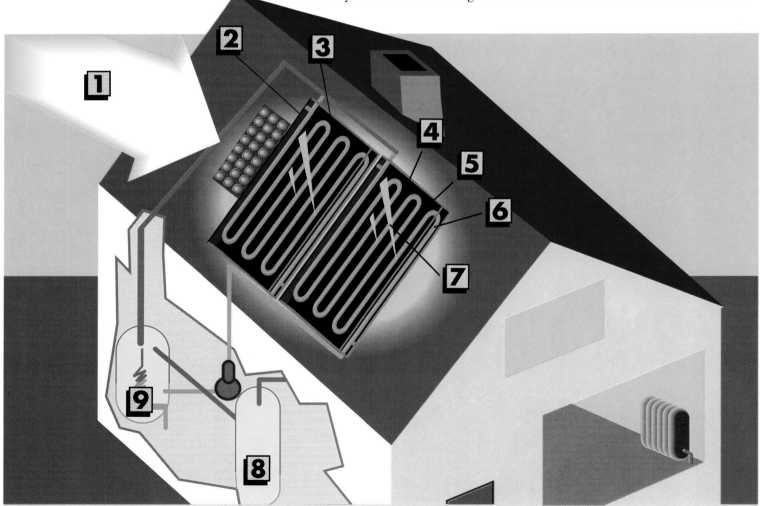

silicon atom in the lower, or *p*-type layer, which is pulled into the upper, or *n*-type layer. An electron in an adjoining atom in the *p*-layer will take the place of the one left. This exchange of electrons creates a current. In this way, a typical cell produces .5 volt of electricity. In order to harness enough power to be useful, solar cells are connected in series of twenty to sixty or more. These cells are packaged together under a glass watertight cover, creating a solar panel.

Most satellites now circling the earth are powered by solar energy, which is also used to recharge their batteries. Solar cells are used to power many smaller items as well, including digital clocks and watches, calculators, radios, televisions, and small battery chargers. There are some home systems that use solar energy for domestic power needs, but these are not yet widespread. Scientists estimate that the cost of supplying electricity to the home using solar energy may drop below the cost of using a public utility as early as the year 2005.

SOLAR HEAT

The most common domestic use of solar energy today is to heat homes, water, and swimming pools. This does not require the use of photovoltaics unless electricity is needed. Most of the sun's energy reaches the earth in the form of light that is really shortwave radiation. That means that the wavelength of the light beam is very short. Not all of this light is visible to the naked eye. When the radiation strikes a solid or liquid, it is absorbed and transformed into heat energy. The material becomes warm, stores the heat, and conducts it to the materials around it (air, water, solids) or reradiates it to other materials of lower temperature.

The most popular type of solar panel for collecting heat is the flat-plate collector. The flat-plate collector absorbs the sun's heat outside the house and transports it inside by means of a transfer medium such as flowing water. This is called active solar heating (as opposed to passive solar heating, which is using windows to collect and window insulation to retain just the right amount of solar radiation to heat, but not overheat, the home or building).

Two of the most popular materials for these flat-plate collectors are aluminum and copper. Although aluminum is less expensive, copper is the more popular of the two because it conducts more heat. Another advantage of copper is that standard plumbing pipes and fittings in the sizes and types usable for solar heating are available at any hardware store. Therefore, standard plumbing tools and methods can be used to make these connections.

A flat-plate collector is made of a gridwork of closely spaced pipes attached to a sheet metal backing called the "plate." The plate and pipes are usually painted with an inexpensive flat black paint for maximum heat absorption.

SOLAR ENERGY

1	rays of sunlight
2	glass cover
3	solar collecting plates
4	black material to absorb heat
5	solar absorber plate
6	copper or aluminum tubing
7	conduction through solar absorber plate or tubing
8	water storage tank
9	heat exchanger

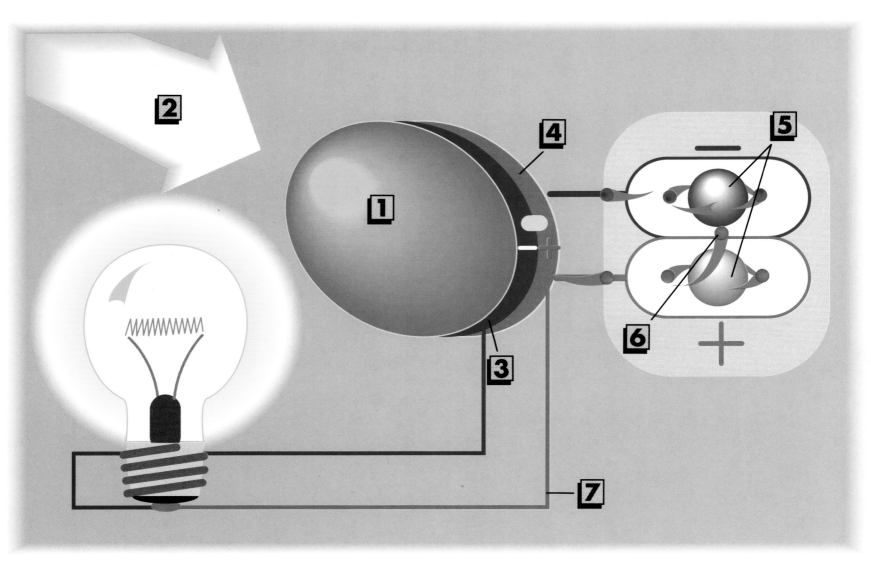

Photovoltaic, or solar, cells turn light into energy using the semiconducting properties of 2 types of silicon. When sunlight strikes the cell, electrons are freed from the silicon atoms. In the diagram, an electron moves from a negatively charged silicon atom to a positively charged atom. The electron flow produces current that can power devices such as calculators, home appliances, and even satellites.

PHOTOVOLTAIC CELLS

1	solar cell
2	sun's rays
3	p-type silicon
4	n-type silicon
5	silicon atoms
6	electron flow
7	current

Visible on this solar heating unit are the black absorber plates. The sun's heat passes through the glass to be absorbed by these metallic, black-coated plates. The heat is then transferred to a fluid that flows through the pipes, visible at the top and bottom of the unit.

The whole assembly is mounted (usually on the roof) in an insulated enclosure with a glass top. The collectors have glass tops because glass easily transmits shortwave radiation, which means that it poses little interference to incoming solar energy. Once the sun's energy has passed through the glass and been absorbed by the material inside, the heat will not be reradiated back outside.

Beneath the cover plate, collectors commonly have another plate that absorbs the sun's infrared rays. This absorber plate is usually made of copper, aluminum, steel, or another suitable material, and is usually coated with a substance—black paint or one of the more sophisticated selective coatings available—that will help it absorb the most heat, rather than reflect or reradiate it.

An array of photovoltaic cells in Hesperia, California provides enough energy to power the town.

From the absorber plate, heat is conducted (transferred) to water or a non-freezing fluid such as ethylene glycol, which flows through the pipes or over the black surface and by the absorber plate, often with the help of a pump or blower. Sometimes, instead of water, air is used. If so, it is blown across the surface of the absorber plate, which has many small irregular surfaces with which the air can come in contact.

Because the sun's heat is conducted from plate to pipes, the entire area of the collector contributes its heat to the water flowing through the pipes. From there on, the system works much like a conventional heating system. The principle of heat transfer is the same. Heat always travels to the cooler water flowing through the pipes, heating the water. (As the fluid is heated, it tends to rise, and cooler fluid flows in to take its place. If the collector is tilted or vertical, as it usually is when mounted on a sloped roof, this effect will move fluid across the collector plate and off without any external help.) The hot water may be used itself or to give off heat to the cooler surroundings, heating the house.

When you push a button on a remote control transmitter, a signal passes to an encoder chip, which in turn sends an electrical signal to the LED. The charge enables electrons to flow, producing infra-red rays, which are transmitted to the receiving unit, which may be a television, CD player, or (as in this diagram) a VCR. A photodiode in the VCR is sensitive to the infra-red rays, which cause electrons to be freed, creating a current. The current produces an electrical signal that passes to a decoder chip, which in turn tells the VCR what to do.

REMOTE SIGNAL IN ACTION
(above)

1	transmitter unit
2	power source
3	button
4	capacitor
5	resistor
6	transistor
7	microchip
8	LED
9	infrared rays to unit
10	photo diode in receiving unit
11	power leads to receiving unit circuitry

REMOTE CONTROL

Remote control allows us to change stations or raise or lower the volume on the TV, fast-forward or reverse the tape in the VCR, or raise and lower the garage door without touching the appliance itself.

When you press a button on a remote-control unit, invisible infrared rays are transmitted to a receiver in the main unit of the appliance. These infrared rays contain a signal in binary code that tells the TV or VCR what to do. The receiver in the main unit picks up the signal and decodes it.

Both the remote-control unit and the receiver contain diodes. A diode is a device that controls the movement of electrons allowing a current to flow in one direction only. Diodes contain p- and n-type atoms (see Solar Energy, page 112). When connected to a positive charge, the p-layer attracts electrons and creates a full current. This is called forward bias. When the connection is reversed, the p-layer allows only a few electrons to move, creating a low current. This is called reverse bias.

Pressing a channel button on a TV remote unit sends a message to an encoder chip, which transforms the signal into electrical pulses in binary code, and sends them to an LED, or light-emitting diode. The LED's forward bias creates a flow of electrons that produce light rays. When the rays reach the receiver unit, they are picked up by another diode called a photodiode, which is sensitive to light. The photodiode is in reverse bias, meaning that a low current is flowing. When struck by light rays, the electrons in the photodiode are excited, and produce an increased current. That current is the signal that is picked up by the decoder, which tells the unit to change the channel.

LED (below)

1	power flow
2	encoder chip
3	electron
4	n-type
5	p-type
6	infrared rays

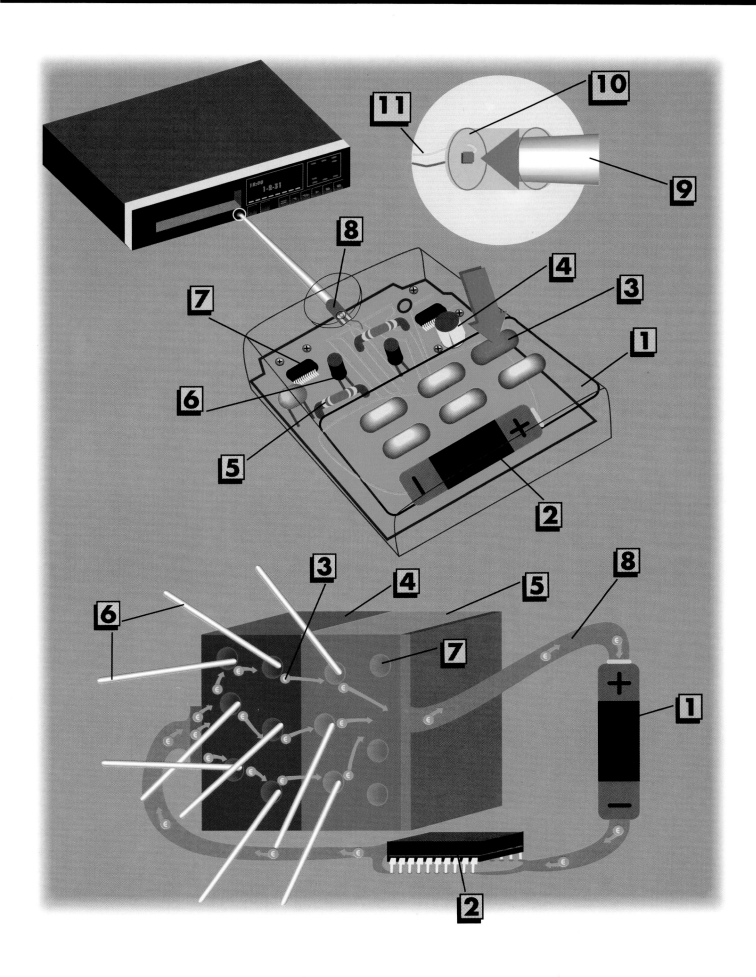

Medtronics, 89
Microwave
  characteristics of, 74, 100
  communication, 74, 110
  cooking with, 100, 101, *103*
  transmission of, 74
Microwave oven, components of, *101*

N

Nuclear Magnetic Resonance (NMR). *See*
  Magnetic Resonance Imaging.

P

Pacemaker
  components of, *88*, 89, 91
  external, first, 89, *91*
  external forces, effect of
    electricity, 90
    magnetism, 97
    metal detectors, 90
    microwaves, 90
  implantation of, 91
  internal, 89, *90*
  inventors of, 89
  operation of, 91
Photovoltaic cell. *See* Solar cell.
Pitch, 18, *19*
  speed control, 16, 20
Polio vaccine, 11
Printing machine, 9

R

Radar, 33, 34-35
Remote control signal, 116-117
Roll, definition of, 18, *19*

S

Satellite
  Communications, 74, 75, 76, 77, 110
    components of, *75*
    early history of, 77
    power sources for, 74, 113
  first, 77
  Weather, 78, *78*

components of, *78*, 79
  GOES (Geostationary Operational
    Environment Satellite) 78
    ability of, 79
    dimensions of, 79
  Landsat, 79
Satellite dish, 74
Solar cells, 74, 114
  creation of electricity by, 112-113
Solar energy, 112
  home heating with, 112, *112*, 113-115
Sonography. *See* Ultrasound.
Space shuttle, *36*, *41*, *42*
  crew quarters, 43, *43*
  engine of, 37, *37*, 40
  external tank (ET), structure of, 40-41,
    42
  flight, explanation of, 42
  ground support, 41
  limitations of, 42-43
  mission profile of, *38-39*
  orbiter
    dimensions of, 37
    thermal protection system (TPS), 37,
      40
  solid rocket boosters (SRBs), 41, 42
Space Transportation System (STS). *See*
  Space shuttle.
Sputnik, 77
Steinberg, Bernard, 35
Supersonic jet. *See* Concorde.
Syncom, 77

T

Tape recorder, *53*
  amplifier, 55
  analog recording
    limitations of, 54
    reproduction of sound, 52, 55
    sound, storage of, 52, 55
  analog tape, *55*
  components, function of, 53-54
  digital audio tape (DAT), 56-58, *57*
    controversy about, 57
    marketing of, 57
    sampling, definition of, 56
  playback, 52
  playback equalization, 54
  tape saturation, 54
Telegraph (igniting model), *8*
Telephone, 9
  cellular, *70*
    cells, 70-71, *72-73*
    cost factors of, 71

mobile telephone switching office
    MTSO), 70-71, *72-73*
Television
  cable transmission of, 108-109, 110-111
  color, 11
  signals, first transmission of, 11
Telstar, 77
Traffic Alert and Collision-Avoidance
  System (TCAS), 33, 35

U

Ultrasound
  medical use of, 86-87
  transducer, 87

V

VCR (Videocassette Recorder), 58
  components of, 61, *60-61*
  playback, 59
  recording with, 59
Vinci, Leonardo da, 14
VSAT (very small aperture terminals), 77

W

Wing. *See* Airfoil.

Y

Yaw, definition of, 18, *19*

Z

Zoll, Dr. Paul, 89

PHOTO CREDITS:

© Evan Agostini, pp. 55, 59, 64, 69, 102, 106

© Carol J. Amato, p. 34

© Christopher Bain, p. 25

Courtesy of British Airways, p. 22

© Bart Barlow/Envision, pp. 50-51

© Simon Feldman/Envision, p. 54

© Robert W. Ginn/Envision, p. 59

© Melabee M. Miller/Envision, p. 70

© Steven Mark Needham/Envision, p. 100

© Ron Erickson, pp. 82-83

© FPG, pp. 98-99

© David Bartruff/FPG, p. 24

© Sal Maimone/FPG, p. 115 top

© Jeffrey Sylvester/FPG, p. 115 bottom

© T. Tracy/FPG, p. 20

Courtesy of GTE Spacenet Corporation, pp. 76-77

Courtesy of Gulfstream Aerospace Corp., pp. 14-16

Courtesy of Hewlett Packard, p. 87

NASA, pp. 36, 37, 40-43, 48-49,

NOAA, pp. 12-13

Courtesy of NEC, p. 71

Courtesy of Rockwell Avionics, pp, 30-31, 35

Courtesy of Siemens, pp. 96-97

Courtesy of Sony Inc, p. 57

Courtesy of Medtronics Inc, pp. 90-91

© Visuals Unlimited, pp. 84-85